INTRODUCTION TO THE ANATOMY and PHYSIOLOGY OF THE SPEECH MECHANISMS

INTRODUCTION TO THE ANATOMY and PHYSIOLOGY OF THE SPEECH MECHANISMS

By

CHARLES F. DIEHL, Ph.D.
Professor of Psychology and Education
Director, Speech and Hearing Center
University of Kentucky
Lexington, Kentucky

CHARLES C THOMAS · PUBLISHER
Springfield · Illinois · U.S.A.

QM 251
.D5

Published and Distributed Throughout the World by
CHARLES C THOMAS • PUBLISHER
BANNERSTONE HOUSE
301-327 East Lawrence Avenue, Springfield, Illinois, U.S.A.
NATCHEZ PLANTATION HOUSE
735 North Atlantic Boulevard, Fort Lauderdale, Florida, U.S.A.

This book is protected by copyright. No part of it may be reproduced in any manner without written permission from the publisher.

© *1968, by* CHARLES C THOMAS • PUBLISHER
Library of Congress Catalog Card Number: 68-25974

With THOMAS BOOKS *careful attention is given to all details of manufacturing and design. It is the Publisher's desire to present books that are satisfactory as to their physical qualities and artistic possibilities and appropriate for their particular use.* THOMAS BOOKS *will be true to those laws of quality that assure a good name and good will.*

Printed in the United States of America
H-19

PREFACE

STUDENTS BEGINNING their study of speech and hearing disorders rarely are aware of the complexity of the territority they are about to enter. For most, speech has appeared so effortless, so uncomplicated, that for them to consider it as a gigantic apparatus composed of hundreds of intricate anatomical parts moved by hundreds of different muscles with bizarre names is to be like the centipede who, when asked to describe the operation of his various legs, became totally immobolized.

The text which follows is, as its title suggests, only an *introduction* to the anatomy and physiology of the speech mechanisms. It should be considered as the first in a series of graded texts covering only the basic fundamental aspects of the highly complicated speech mechanisms. The object here is, primarily, to map all of the territory and to guide the student through it without too much struggle along the way. (And for the student with no previous exposure to the biological sciences even the simplified route will seem difficult enough.) Complicated details, which for some might block the view entirely, have been avoided wherever possible. And only time will tell whether, by attempting to provide a clear view of the forest, too many trees have been removed!

Throughout the text little or no attention is given to associating various units to pathological speech and hearing problems. Only in a few instances in relation to various theoretical concepts have several speech pathologies been mentioned. The avoidance of clinical associations has been deliberate. The average student, we believe, should concentrate first on the normal speech apparatus. Once this is understood and reflected upon, the various pathologies, we have found, can be related far more meaningfully. To undertake both simultaneously, however, seems unrealistic in terms of the amount of time normally devoted to a course in the anatomy and physiology of the speech mechanisms.

The writer wishes to express appreciation to his students who, by their questions and suggestions throughout the years, have helped in assembling the material appearing in the text. He wishes also to express special appreciation to Mrs. Janet Ramsey for her help with editing and typing and to Julian Cohen for his assistance with the illustrations.

Lexington, Kentucky CHARLES F. DIEHL

CONTENTS

INTRODUCTION TO THE ANATOMY and PHYSIOLOGY OF THE SPEECH MECHANISMS

Chapter 1

THE HUMAN BODY

THE NEED TO KNOW

STUDENTS BEGINNING the study of speech pathologies are sometimes disgruntled at having to learn in considerable detail the structural and functional components of the speech apparatus. "But it's so impractical," is a common complaint. "When I work with a child's articulation defect," they say, "what good will it do me to know the names of the muscles of the tongue or lips?"

We sympathize! Students are often required to "learn" (memorize) a vast array of information without being provided with motivation for their efforts. The instructor's attitude, if it dares be questioned, very often is, "Look, I'm the boss. If I tell you to learn it, learn it; or else!" The words may be different—not so blunt perhaps—but the student gets the point. He realizes his is ". . . not to reason why. . . ."

Much information presented in the average college classroom is obviously impractical and can never be actively applied in problem solving. It is all part of what is called a liberal education. And it is not our intent to condemn it and insist it be eliminated. What we do believe, however, is that a student deserves to know *why* information is being presented and *why* he will be expected to evaluate it, be aware of it, compare it, think with it creatively, or do whatever it is hoped he will eventually do with it.

So let us return to the student who objected to the impracticality of knowing the muscles of the tongue and lips. This student and others, apparently, were never given the kind of initial information we have just been discussing. And it is for this reason we have chosen to open this text with a fairly detailed discussion of why a speech pathologist needs to know the anatomy and physiology of the speech apparatus. For if in the beginning the serious student has not been convinced of its importance, he cannot be blamed later for being disinterested and lacking in motivation.

ORAL SPEECH DEFINED

Oral speech*, experts agree, is a psychophysiological system utilizing various parts of the body and various parts of the mind to communicate information. *Respiration* (to initiate sound), *phonation* (to produce sound), *resonation* (to amplify and enrich sound), and *articulation* (to shape sounds into words) are the terms used to identify the four basic physical processes; *integration* is used to identify the psychic activity — the sensory perceptions, symbolic processes, generalization formulation and the final innervation of appropriate motor impulses to activate the entire system in order to speak.

The beginning student, probably, has rarely thought of speech in terms of the above definition. He has, in most cases, heard speech from the beginning spoken so fluently and with such apparent little effort that he has had no reason to suppose that it was, indeed, an extremely complicated machine capable of breaking down or of being defective to start with. And yet the definition leaves no doubt. To speak is to use body and mind in an extremely complex, highly integrated, yet apparently effortless way.

Speech is often described as an *overlaid* or *secondary* process. Like no other system in the human body, speech involves structures whose primary purposes are for sustaining life. There is no part of the human body used for speech whose original purpose was for speech alone. Only by accident, or the ingenuity of man, apparently, were the same parts utilized to produce speech. This can easily be illustrated by considering the respiratory system. Without breath there would be no initiation of sound and therefore no speech; however, without the exchange of gases occurring via respiration there would be nothing at all. No life to speak!

Some aspects of the total speech process, it should be noted here, are comparatively easy to identify, classify and evaluate. And because of this, perhaps, the tendency has been to oversimplify—to supply simple answers to complex questions. The voice variables,

---

*The term *speech* is used throughout as the oral production of the sounds (phonemes) comprising words. *Language* is used as the system of symbols used to represent information. Speech communicates language orally.

for example: rate, pitch, quality, intensity, inflection, interval, intonation, phrasing, fluency and articulation among others may be identified and appraised fairly accurately by a trained listener, sometimes with and sometimes without the aid of measuring instruments available commercially. Often, however, the speech appraisal ends there. The speech clinician hears the kind of error and without further analysis wants to correct it immediately. And so the challenging business of relating the various uses or misuses of the speech variables to the underlying anatomical and psychical architecture of the speaker frequently remains undone.

No one, of course, would argue that what we are suggesting is simple or even entirely possible at the moment. Knowledge of neurological functioning is only slowly being accumulated. There are still huge gaps! Not only neurologists, however, are having difficulties. Anatomists, after years of study, also continue to disagree, among other things, on the functioning of the vocal cords. Only recently have psychiatrists begun seriously to equate certain speech defects with abnormal psychic behavior.

Realizing the difficulties, yet assuming he has been convinced of the need to know, what goals can the beginning student hope to achieve in studying the anatomy and physiology of the speech apparatus?

Two goals, it seems logical, can be achieved. First, a great deal *is* known about the anatomy and physiology of speech. This information can be studied, and in many instances of speech defectiveness it can be applied in determining cause and programming remediation. Second, it will become evident to the student how much remains unknown. Learning how to ask pertinent questions is as important, sometimes, as learning how to answer them. Further, knowing what is unknown can sometimes be of immense value when discussing problems or programming speech therapy for various individuals. Specialists from other professions—especially physicians—will frequently request information from the speech pathologist. The speech pathologist will be expected to know, or not know, whichever the case may be.

In the final analysis the speech pathologist is normally expected in his professional capacity to do the following:

1. Evaluate for kind and degree of speech disorder.

2. Determine cause by appraising the malfunctioning of the speech apparatus.
3. Make a prognosis.
4. Establish realistic programs for remediation.
5. Recommend and/or provide remedial techniques.

We believe the first item on this list may be accomplished by the speech pathologist with little or no real understanding of the speech apparatus. However, we also believe this will be as far as his competencies will permit him to go *with assurance.* He may be advised by others, he may recommend proven techniques for similar cases, but he will never feel totally confident unless he can see beneath to the basic parts of the speech system, and above to the superstructure moving the parts.

BASIC TERMINOLOGY

For those who have had no basic courses in the biological sciences, it will be essential before moving into the territory to be explored to learn the common terms used in referring to body parts and to drawings of them. There may be little fascination and small satisfaction, we agree, with an initial step of learning different words for "front" and "back," "above" and "below." However, it is very difficult either to describe or visualize the location of anatomical parts, or drawings of them, without being familiar with the basic nomenclature. In addition to the terms mentioned below, others will be found in the Glossary at the end of this text.

Planes

When the human body is upright with the upper limbs at the sides and the palms facing forward it is said to be in anatomical position, or the reference position for the various planes (sections) into which the body may be divided. There are three primary planes: *sagittal, frontal* and *transverse.*

A *sagittal* plane divides the body into right and left portions. If the division is exactly in the midline of the body and the right and left halves are equal the plane is called *midsaggital* or *median.*

A *frontal* (coronal) plane divides the body into front and back portions.

A *transverse* (horizontal) plane divides the body into upper and lower portions.

Position

In describing the position of various anatomical structures, those toward the front of the body or nearest the abdominal surface are called *anterior* or *ventral;* toward the back, *posterior* or *dorsal.* (In quadrupeds, anterior refers to the head end, and ventral to the abdominal or lower surface. Posterior refers to the tail end, and dorsal to the back.)

Structures in the upper portion of the body or higher than others are *superior.* Those in the lower portion, or lower than others, are *inferior.*

Other terms used are *medial,* nearer the midline of the body and *lateral,* farther away from the midline. *Proximal,* in referring to a limb, means a position nearer the trunk or central axis; *distal,* a more peripheral (away from trunk) position. *Cranial* or *cephalic* means nearest or toward the head; *caudal* means away from the head. *Afferent* in referring to nerves or blood vessels means conducting toward the structure or organ; *efferent* means conducting away from the structure or organ. All terms are outlined in Table I.

The examination of the surface of a bone reveals many projections and depressions. For example, a *process* is a general term for any bony prominence. *Tubercle* is a small rounded projection. *Crest* is a prominent ridge. Table II lists terms related to bone structure.

In addition to basic terminology, for the student with little or no orientation to the architecture of the human body, the following section presents the human body in a very general way and should supply sufficient information for identifying those parts and systems directly involved in speech production.

THE HUMAN BODY IN GENERAL

Man belongs to a group of animals known as vertebrates (having a backbone or vertebral column). He has a bilateral symmetry about his body with two sides being mirror images of each other.

TABLE I

Descriptive Terms Used in Anatomy

Terms	*Name*	*Explanation*	
Plane or section	Sagittal	Vertical plane or section dividing body into right and left portions	
	Midsagittal	Vertical at midline; dividing body into right and left halves	
	Frontal or Coronal	Vertical, but at right angles to sagittal sections, dividing body into anterior (front) and posterior (back) portions	
	Transverse	Horizontal, hence at right angles to both sagittal and frontal sections, dividing body into upper and lower portions	
		Man	*Quadruped*
Surface or relative position	Anterior or Ventral	Front of body, hence on or nearest abdominal surface	Anterior—head end Ventral—abdominal or lower surface
	Posterior or Dorsal	Back of body	Posterior—tail end Dorsal—back
	Superior	Upper or higher	
	Inferior	Lower	
Relative position or direction	Cranial (Craniad) or Cephalic (Cephalad)	Nearest or toward the head	
	Caudal (Caudad)	Away from the head	
	Medial (Mesad)	Middle or nearest the midsagittal plane	
	Lateral (Laterally)	Side or farthest from midsagittal plane	
	Proximal (Proximally)	Near the source or attachment	
	Distal (Distally)	Away from source or attachment	
	Afferent	In relation to nerves or blood vessels—conducting toward structure or organ	
	Efferent	Conducting away from structure or organ	

TABLE II

Terms Applied to Bones

	Elevation and Projections
condyle	rounded process, usually smooth for articulation
crest	ridge
head	expanded end of a bone
process	any elevation or projection
spine	pointed process
trochanter	very large process
trochlea	process shaped like pulley
tubercle	small, rounded projection
tuberosity	larger, roughened projection
	Depressions, Grooves, Openings, Concavities
aditus	entrance into a cavity
alveolus	deep pit or socket
anirum	a sinus
facet	small, flat surface
fissure	slit like opening
foramen	opening through which blood vessels or other structures pass
fossa	depression
hiatus	slit or gap
meatus	short canals
sinus	cavity in interior of a bone, lined with mucous membrane and filled with air
sulcus	groove or narrow elongated concavity
	Other Terms
fontanelle	membranous space between cranial bones in fetal life and infancy
remus	part of bone forming an angle with body of the bone
suture	line of junction between five adjacent bones of the skull

Body Cavities

The gross structure of man can be thought of initially in terms of cavities and bones. The internal body structure is characterized by two major cavities, the *dorsal* cavity and the *ventral* cavity (see Fig. 1). The large dorsal cavity is divided into the *cranial* cavity formed by the skull bones and containing the brain; and the *vertebral* cavity formed by the vertebrae and containing the spinal cord.

The ventral cavity is divided into the *thoracic* and *abdominopelvic* cavities by the diaphragm. Additional smaller cavities comprise the thoracic cavity: the pericardial cavity contains the heart, and the pleural cavities contain the lungs. Lying between the subdivisions of the thoracic cavity are the trachea, bronchi, esophagus, thymus gland, and blood and lymph vessels.

The abdominopelvic cavity is continuous; however, it is generally thought of in terms of the upper abdominal and lower pelvic portions.

The abdominal portion contains the liver, gallbladder, stomach, spleen, pancreas, small and large intestines and kidneys. The pelvic portion contains the bladder, rectum and sigmoid colon. In females, in addition, there is the uterus, uterine tubes and ovaries; in males, the prostate gland, the seminal vesicles and part of ductus deferens. The organs in the thoracic and abdominopelvic cavities are frequently referred to as *viscera.*

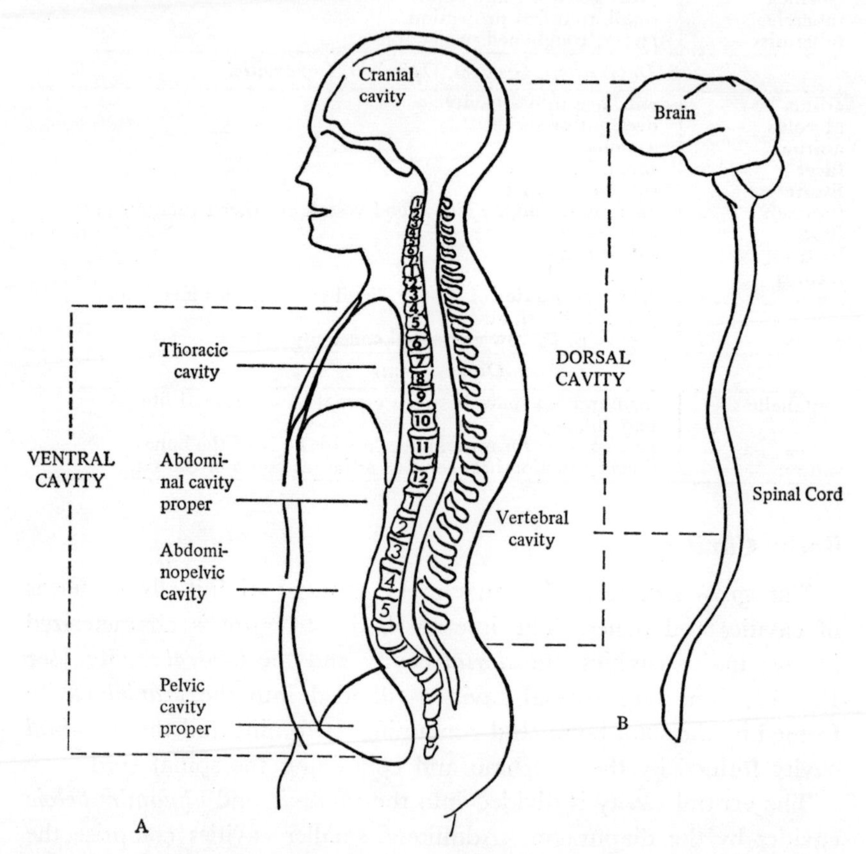

FIGURE 1. Body cavities as seen in a midsagittal section of head and trunk. *(A)* Diagram of midsagittal section of head and trunk, showing vertebral column and body cavities. *(B)* Organs of the dorsal cavity.

Divisions of the Skeleton

The bones of the body fall into two major groups. Those comprising the *axial* skeleton, and those forming the *appendicular* skeleton. The axial is composed of the bones of the skull, vertebral column and thorax; the appendicular, of the bones of upper and lower extremities.

At different ages, the number of bones in the skeleton varies. At birth, the human body contains about 270 bones. During infancy,

TABLE III

Bones of the Body

Axial Skeleton

Skull	
Cranium (single bones) 4	Face (single bones) 2
Occipital	Mandible
Frontal	Vomer
Sphenoid	
Ethmoid	Face (paired) 12
	Maxilla
Cranium (paired) 4	Zygomatic
Parietal	Lacrimal
Temporal	Nasal
	Inferior nasal concha
Ear ossicles (paired) 6	Palatine
Malleus	
Incus	Throat (single) 1
Stapes	Hyoid
	Total 29
*Vertebral column** (single) 26*	
Cervical 7 (first called *Atlas*)	
Thoracic 12	
Lumbar 5	
Sacral 1	
Coccyx 1	*Total* 26
Thorax (single) 1	Thorax (paired) 24
Sternum	Ribs
	Total 25
	Total Axial 80

*Appendicular Skeleton***

Upper Extremities	*Lower Extremities*
Shoulder—Scapula, Clavicle 4	Hip, Pelvic Girdle—
Upper arm—Humerous 2	Innominate bone (Ilium, Pubis, Ischium) 2
Forearm—Ulna, Radium 4	Thigh—Femur 2
Wrist—Carpus 16	Kneecap—Patella 2
Hand—Metacarpus 10	Leg—Tibia, Fibula 4
Fingers & Thumb—Phalanges 28	Ankle—Tarsus 14
	Foot—Metatarsus 10
	Toes—Phalanges 28
Total Upper 64	*Total Lower* 62
	Total Appendicular 126

*The nine or ten terminal segments which fuse to form the sacrum and coccyx are counted as two bones.

**All bones are paired in this division. Numbers listed are totals.

this number is slightly reduced by the union of some separate segments to form single bones. From then on, however, through puberty the number increases as the epiphyses and bones of the wrists and ankles develop. After puberty, reduction again occurs by a gradual union of independent bones. Finally, the adult human consists of 206 bones.

The outline of the various bones in Table III may be helpful in understanding the total skeletal structure. Some bones, of course, may be of little or no importance in relation to the speech apparatus. However, in the organismic (mind-body) approach to studying human behavior quite frequently a knowledge of the total skeletal system, at least in a general way, may be helpful. For example, a physiologist a number of years ago seriously considered studying with x-ray the number of carpals in the wrists of children with articulation disorders. Those with defects, he postulated, might demonstrate a general skeletal lack of maturation as compared with

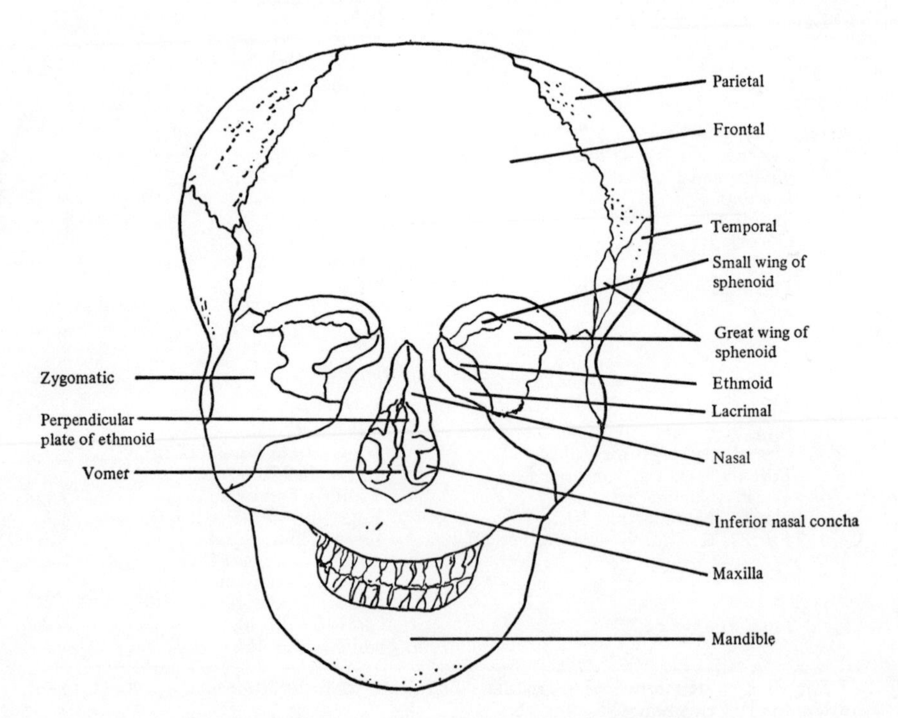

FIGURE 2. Anterior view of the skull showing bones.

a control group of normal-speaking children. Some work has already been done in this area in relation to reading disorders (Park, 1964).

Body Organization

The skeletal structure and the cavities formed by the various bones of the body comprise only one aspect of the human. Another aspect of the vertebrate is its progressive organization from cells into tissues, organs and finally systems.

Cells

Cells are the central core of the human structure. The cell is an organized mass of protoplasm surrounded by a membrane. Unfortunately, the living secrets of protoplasm are unknown because chemical analysis makes it lifeless. However, it is known that all cells have a life span varying with their function. For example, red blood cells have a life span of four months; white, only a few weeks. Nerve cells normally live as long as the individual, while gland and skin cells are perishing and being replaced constantly. Some devote their lives to the scientific study of cells called *cytology.*

Tissues

Tissue is the combining of similar cells for certain functions; its scientific study is called *histology.* Tissue is commonly classified by function: *epithelial, connective, muscular,* and *nervous.*

Epithelial tissue lines the inner walls of the cavities mentioned previously and covers the outer surface of the body. Glands and parts of sense organs are specialized epithelial structures. The vocal folds are composed of epithelial tissue.

Connective tissue connects or binds various body structures, and assists with body repair, nutrition and regeneration. There are five major types of connective tissue: *tendon, ligament, aponeurosis, cartilage,* and *bone.* Typical of tendons, ligaments and aponeuroses are *collagenous* fibers, so called because they yield a substance called collagen upon boiling. These long, flexible fibers are multidirectional; however, they lack extensibility, and are therefore found in strong, but not particularly stretchable, tendons connecting muscles to bones, and in ligaments connecting bones to bones. Occassionally the fibers are organized into broad sheets called *aponeuroses.* The *palatine aponeurosis,* for example, is a broad band of tissue covering the soft palate.

Not all connective tissue is collagenous. Some contains *elastin* and shows a high degree of elasticity which, however, decreases with age. Hollow organs, for example the esophagus, trachea, bronchial tubes and the larynx, contain membranes composed of elastic tissue.

Sometimes connective tissue hardens to *cartilage* in specific regions. The most common type of cartilage called hyaline resembles rubber, is flexible, slightly elastic and semitransparent. The costal cartilages and some cartilages of the larynx, nose and respiratory passages are hyaline. On the other hand, the corniculate and cuneiform cartilages in the larynx are composed of more elastic fibers. Elastic cartilages also occur in the external auditory canal, epiglottis, and eustachian tubes.

Bone, of course, is the densest of all connective tissues. The various bones of the body have been mentioned previously, and the anatomical terms used to describe parts of them listed in Table II.

Muscular tissue corresponds to the various types of muscles. It can be *smooth* (plain, involuntary, unstriated) *skeletal* (striated, voluntary) and *cardiac* (heart). Contractility is the most outstanding aspect of muscular tissue, with the contraction occurring only in the direction corresponding to the long axis of the cells. Other aspects of muscular tissue are irritability, conductivity, elasticity and viscosity.

Muscle activity, as we shall see later, is of immense importance in the speech process as well as in other body activities. Voluntary muscles, for example, enable man to maintain erect posture and to hold and move his extremities in various positions. Skeletal contracture provides for locomotion to obtain food, escape danger and to communicate by speech, facial expression, signal or body attitude. It is essential for breathing, for vision, hearing and for maintaining body temperature. In the digestive system, smooth muscle activity propels ingested substances, body fluids and excretions from place to place. And finally, cardiac muscle pumps blood to all body tissues.

Nervous tissue consists essentially of *neurons,* or nerve cells, which are active, irritable and conducting units, as well as *neurologia* cells which play a passive role as supporting framework. The neuron will be discussed in considerable detail in Chapter 2.

Organs

Tissues combine to form organs. Each organ, however, is a functional unit developed from two or more tissues. The tongue and larynx, for examples, both important organs in the speech apparatus, have tissues as their next simpler component. The larynx, for example, contains epithelium, connective tissue, muscles, nerves and blood vessels.

Systems

Organizations of closely allied organs united for a common purpose are called systems. Systems include the circulatory, endocrine, excretory, digestive, integumentary, muscular, nervous, reproductive, respiratory and skeletal. We believe that eventually speech may logically be listed along with the others since it, too, is an organization of organs working together.

Joints

In connection with basic bodily structure some mention should be made of the *joints* which hold the entire structure together and enable various parts to move. There are two major types of joints: *synarthrosis* and *diarthrosis.*

Synarthroses, generally speaking, are immovable or slightly movable—the absence of a cavity at the joint preventing extensive movement. The teeth, for example, insert into the mandible and maxilla via this type of joint.

There are several subtypes in this category. In the skull, the various bone ends are serrated and approximated by fibrous tissue. In *synchondroses,* between ribs and costal cartilages, the bone ends are approximated by cartilage. In *syndemoses,* between spinous processes and laminae of adjacent vertebrae, the connection is via dense fibrous connective tissue deposited in the form of ligaments. In *symphyses,* between bodies of adjacent vertebrae, ends of bones are covered with cartilage and separated by an intercartilage disk. Approximation in this instance is through a fibrous capsule.

Diarthroses constitute most of the bodily joints. Diverse movement is possible with diarthroses for there is a joint cavity surrounded by a fibrous tissue called the articular capsule. The internal layer of the capsule secretes a tiny amount of synovial fluid into the cavity to lubricate the joint. In areas of considerable friction bursae containing synovial fluid appear, providing for smoother movement of muscles and tendons over bony prominences. Painful *bursitis* is thought in some cases to be directly related to the drying up of the fluid at critical points of articulation. The vast movement possible with diarthroses is illustrated by the activity of the arytenoid cartilages in the larynx to which the vocal folds are attached. The arytenoids are capable of moving clockwise and counterclockwise; laterally or medially; tilting forward or backward.

Chapter 2

THE NERVOUS SYSTEM

NORMAL SPEECH RESULTS from an integration of activity so, to appraise it and evaluate available relevant information, it is necessary to consider, at least in a simplified, general way, the integrating structure—the nervous system. By looking at the various parts of the nervous system first, the physical processes involved in speech (respiration, phonation, resonation, articulation) will, we believe, be less complicated, for neurological information can be included as each is discussed in turn.

Neuroanatomy and neurophysiology are usually preperceived by most students beginning their study as extremely difficult and largely incomprehensible. Nevertheless, they recognize the fascination in attempting to understanding these areas, no matter what the level of understanding, for here roots all behavior.

No one will deny the complexity of a neurophysiology where speculation rather than factual evidence may have to provide operational viewpoints for many years to come; however, the student will discover neuroanatomy, or the names and locations of various structures in the nervous system, to be less difficult. It is a new language, yet, once learned, it may be sufficient to motivate the student to pioneer eventually; to take a step, no matter how small, in the direction of clarifying the many obscurities surrounding the neurophysiology of speech.

The nervous system constitutes the link between the external environment and the many physiologic and psychologic mechanisms enabling man to adjust to his world. Sudden environmental changes stimulate advantageously located sensory receptors of the nervous system. The resulting impulses travel centrally over sensory nerves, through various connections and finally to end organs, bringing about a response. In addition to receiving information and acting upon it in an organized way, the central nervous system apparently records and correlates both stimulus and response, so that man eventually builds up a background of experience, or a frame of reference, enabling him to select future courses of action with increasing skill.

The nervous system also plays a prominent role in integrating adjustments to changes in the internal environment. Thus, the total response is coordinated, made up of many separate parts constituting a vast array of physical and psychic mechanisms. Conversational speech, for example, is normally so well integrated one usually is totally unaware of the processes involved, or the energy being expended.

Nervous Tissue

Nervous tissue, the fabric of the nervous system, consists essentially of neurons, or nerve cells, which are the active, irritable and conducting units, and neurologia cells which make up the supporting framework. The *neuron,* composed of a cell body and one or more processes, is the structural unit of the nervous system.

The Neuron—Cell Body

The cell body of the neuron has a spherical nucleus in which there is a conspicuous mass, or nucleolus, but very little chromatin (found in most other cells). The cytoplasm (protoplasm) consists of homogeneous material in which fine neurofibrils and Nissl bodies are embedded. The delicate neurofibrils cross the cytoplasm and extend into all the processes. The Nissl bodies are granular masses of ribonucleic acid (RNA) which stain brightly with basic aniline dyes. These granules disintegrate upon injury to the cell body or its processes.

Processes of the Neuron

Nerve cells may be classified according to the number of cytoplasmic processes extending from the cell body as *unipolar, bipolar* and *multipolar*. Typical unipolar neurons are not, however, found in man. The cells of the spinal ganglia, making up the sensory or afferent components of the spinal nerves, and the ganglia cells of the cranial nerves appear to be unipolar cells since they seem to have only a single process. (Both spinal and cranial nerves are part of the *peripheral nervous system* which is discussed in detail in Chapter 3). These cells, however, are primitive bipolar cells in which eccentric growth has caused what were originally two processes to fuse as they emerge from a cell body. Bipolar cells, in which two processes may be seen leaving the cell separately, are found only in the ganglia of the two branches of the eighth cranial or auditory nerve, in one layer of the retina of the eye, and in the olfactory receptors. Unipolar and bipolar cells are sensory nerve cells. The multipolar neurons, having more than two processes, show considerable variation in detailed structure and furnish the general pattern for the majority of neurons. Motor nerve cells are multipolar. *Internuncial* or *associational* neurons transmitting impulses from one neuron to another within the spinal cord and brain are also multipolar.

All but one of the cell processes of the neuron are *dendrites* conducting impulses *toward the cell body.* From the Greek word meaning "tree" the dendrite has many branches spreading out like those of a tree. Both bipolar and multipolar neurons have only one *axon.* The axon conducts impulses *away from the cell body.*

Covering of Nerve Fibers

Nerve fibers are the processes of the nerve cells. Many covered with a layer of lipid material called *myelin* are called *myelinated* or *medullated.* The myelin sheath is broken at intervals into segments called *nodes of Ranvier.* Myelinated fibers are found in abundance in the cerebrospinal nerves and in the white matter of the brain and spinal cord. Unmyelinated fibers are found in the autonomic nerves and occasionally among afferent fibers of cerebrospinal nerves.

Peripheral nerve fibers have an outer covering composed of a thin membrane called *neurilemma.* This membrane covers the myelin sheath and is continuous across the nodes of Ranvier. Unmyelinated peripheral nerves also have a covering of neurilemma. The neurilemma covering may account for the regeneration of peripheral nerves which occurs in some cases of injury. Nerve fibers within the brain and cord with no neurilemma never regenerate when injured.

Myelin sheath, apparently, is related to the conduction of nerve impulses since transmission is always more rapid in myelinated than in unmyelinated fibers.

Neuron as Structural Unit of Nervous Impulses

A nerve impulse starts in a dendrite of a receptor (sensory nerve ending) and travels through the cell body and out of the axon. The impulse then crosses the contiguous boundary between axon and dendrite (the synapse) to contact the dendrite of the next neuron. It continues through the cell body and the axon of the second neuron then across the synapse to the dendrite of the third neuron, and so on and on in a continuous chain. In transmitting nerve impulses, however, the neuron is not restricted to a single route; it may conduct the impulse to several other neurons at one and the same time through its connections with them. While the nerve impulse usually is conducted from the axon end of each neuron across the synapse, to the dendrite of the next neuron, once activated, a nerve fiber can conduct equally well in either direction (antidromic conduction).

The Nerve Impulse

Nerve impulses are initiated by receptors in response to changes in internal or external environment.

A stimulus, to be effective in bringing about a response in excitable nervous tissue, must have certain characteristics as follows: (1) It must be of sufficient strength; (2) The rate of change of the environmental conditions of the cell imposed by the stimulus must be sufficiently rapid, and (3) The stimulus must be applied for a certain minimum duration. For example, if you touched an electrical wire and received a shock of from four to five milliamperes, not only would you feel it, but also the muscles of your hand would contract violently. However, if the intensity was reduced to below one milliampere you would neither feel it nor would your muscles contract.

There are four types of environmental changes frequently imposed experimentally to elicit a response: *mechanical* (striking, pinching, sharp blow); *thermal* (sudden change in temperature); *chemical*

(chemical change in chemical environment of cell), and *radiant* (artificial light or infrared lamp).

Character of the Nerve Impulse

When an impulse elicited by one of the means just described sweeps along a nerve fiber, there is a burst of electrical activity called the *action potential.* These action potentials or waves within the brain may be visualized by using the cathode-ray oscillograph. The resulting record is called an electroencephalogram (EEG)—used sometimes to determine the cause of certain speech disorders.

Neurons transmit impulses at different speeds and at different intensities and possess varying thresholds of response. For example, the neurons making up the hypoglossal nerve (C-XII) innervating the front of the tongue are said to have five times the speed of conduction as the nerve to the soft palate. The tongue nerve will respond at one-fourth the threshold of the palatal nerve, or the palatal nerve requires a stimulus four times as great to activate it. Case histories of children in the elementary grades with articulation defects occasionally show familial patterns of articulation defects along with poor motor coordination. A defensible hypothesis for etiology in these cases is that the threshold of excitation of the nerves innervating at least some of their speech organs is high and the rate of conduction slow—an inherited tendency.

Neurons are fatigable. After an impulse has been transmitted, the neuron cannot be stimulated again immediately. Although it has been argued that some nerves related to postural tone, for example, continue to be stimulated indefinitely—a logical argument when one thinks for a moment about standing up in a certain position—some consider it more probable that postural tone is maintained by the alternate stimulation of different groups of closely related neurons.

Neurons must sometimes summate their strength or action potentials to cross the synapse. A fairly light touch on the shoulder may occasionally not evoke a response until several neurons carrying the impulse have combined sufficiently to jump the synapse between sensory and motor neurons. Why this occurs is not known.

Nerve networks exhibit the phenomena of recruitment. Repeated stimuli appearing at the moment when a nerve is somewhat excitable may recruit fibers and thus produce a response when a single stimulus was unsuccessful. These stimuli may come from widely separated sources, i.e., ears or eyes. The deft fingers of the professional pickpocket might therefore be experienced upon entrance into the unsuspecting victim's pocket only if, simultaneously, someone whispered, "You're being robbed."

A nerve impulse derives no energy from an initiating stimulus. If the stimulus reaches threshold—one just strong enough to initiate activity—the nerve fiber responds to the maximum of its potential. A stronger impulse to the same fiber accomplishes no more. This phenomenon is known as the *All or Nothing Law.* No matter with how much or little energy you pull the trigger of a gun the response is always the same.

Nerves and Nerve Tracts

Nerves are the white, cablelike structures located outside the brain and spinal cord over which the nerve impulses travel similar to the way electrical waves travel over electrical wires. A *nerve* consists of nerve processes (fibers) grouped in bundles, or *fasciculi,* together with their blood vessels and lymphatic vessels and various fiber coverings. A nerve is a collection of processes visible to the naked eye but *each process* is too small to be seen by the naked eye, and hundreds or thousands are necessary to form a nerve. Bundles of nerve processes may be connected within a single nerve, or the fibers may divide into branches connecting with other nerves to form a nerve network, or *plexus.*

Inside the spinal cord and brain, when nerve processes connect to form bundles, they are called *tracts* rather than nerves. In the cord, *ascending, afferent* (sensory) tracts carry impulses to the brain; *descending, efferent* (motor) tracts carry impulses from the brain. In the brain, *projection* fibers connect the cerebral cortex to lower centers in the hindbrain or the spinal cord; *commissural* fibers connect both sides of the brain; *association* fibers connect brain areas on the same side.

Injury to a group of projection tracts, for example, in the internal capsule in the diencephalon of the forebrain may result in paralysis.

Efferent nerves may be *motor,* carrying impulses to voluntary muscles; *secretory,* carrying impulses to glands; *accelerator,* carrying impulses that stimulate activity of visceral or cardiac muscles; or *inhibitor,* carrying impulses to retard or stop activity of visceral or cardiac muscles.

Divisions of the Nervous System

The nervous system conveying the various impulses just described can be divided into three major divisions: the *central* containing the brain and the spinal cord; the *peripheral* containing the *cranial* and *spinal* nerves; and the *autonomic* containing the *sympathetic* and *parasympathetic* divisions. The autonomic is often considered an anatomical extension of the peripheral division rather than a separate system. Functionally, however, they are markedly different.

THE CENTRAL NERVOUS SYSTEM— BRAIN AND SPINAL CORD

The Brain

The brain lies within the skull in the cranial cavity (see Fig. 1). Numerous openings, or foramina, in the base of the skull provide for passage of blood vessels and nerves through the skull to lower centers. The *foramen magnum,* a large opening at the base of the skull, enables the spinal cord to be continuous with the brain.

The Meninges

Surrounding and protecting both the brain and the cord are layers of nonnervous tissue collectively called meninges. The outer layer is *dura mater,* a tough, fibrous membrane, the first meningeal layer encountered when bone is removed prior to neural surgery. In certain regions the dura mater contains channels or sinuses carrying venous blood (deficient in oxygen and laden with carbon dioxide) from the brain via veins in the neck to the heart.

Just internal to the dura mater is a thin membrane called the *arachnoid.* Finally, around the brain a delicate network of connective tissue connects the arachnoid to the innermost meningeal layer, the *pia mater.* The space between the arachnoid and pia mater, the *subarachnoid space,* contains the cerebrospinal fluid discussed on page 33. It should be noted that, since the meninges surround both the brain and spinal cord, the cerebrospinal fluid is available for examination via a spinal tap or lumbar puncture—frequently performed to determine focus or type of neural injury.

Divisions of the Brain

Numerous terms have been used by neurologists and others to describe the various parts of the brain. As many as possible are included in the following discussion to avoid confusion for the student who may be reading other references.

During the course of embryonic development the nervous system becomes a tubular structure. The part of the tube to develop in the head forms the brain. Three enlargements of the tube are found in early development—the *forebrain, midbrain* and *hindbrain.*

The Forebrain

The forebrain, or *cerebrum,* forms the *telencephalon* or *endbrain,* and the *diencephalon* or *interbrain.*

The Telencephalon. The telencephalon gives rise to the two cerebral hemispheres forming the bulk of the brain. Here motor, sensory, and higher mental activities of all kinds are known to be located. The huge size of the hemispheres in comparison with other areas of the brain is, apparently, related to the use to which these vital behavior centers have been put. It is interesting to note how man from outer space is usually conceived by science-fiction writers as having enormous hemispheres tending to dominate the total anatomical structure. The reasoning behind this conjecture probably envisons a man from Mars as being far ahead of Earth man in all forms of mental development. Thus, having used the forebrain more, he will therefore possess much larger hemispheres.

The two hemispheres are divided by a prominent fissure (groove), the *great longitudinal fissure,* which is occupied by a downward projection of dura mater, the *falx cerebri.* The surface of the hemispheres, it can be seen when the arachnoid and pia mater are removed, are folded or convoluted. Convolutions are called *gyri;* the depressions or valleys between gyri are called *sulci,* or *fissures.* The most prominent of these are shown in Figure 3.

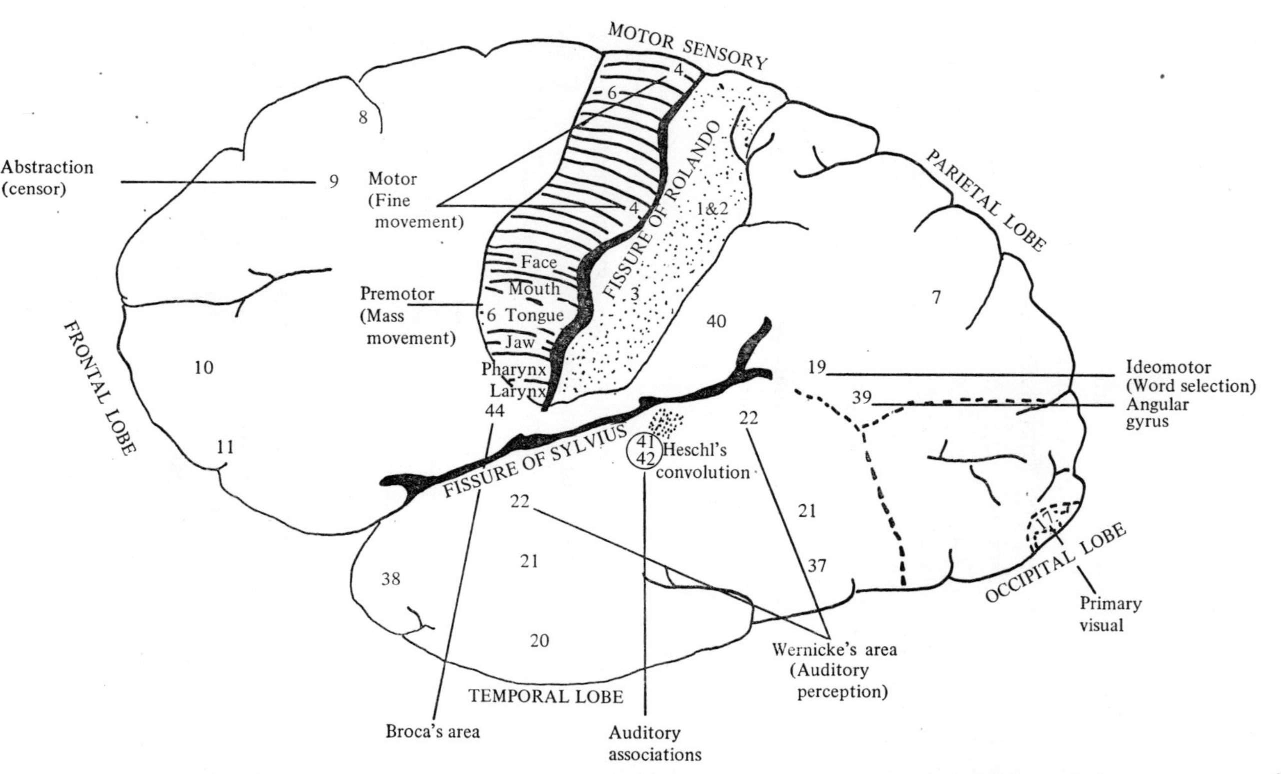

FIGURE 3. Left hemisphere with fissures, lobes, and some of Brodmann's numbered subdivisions of the cortex shown. Areas thought to be related to audition and speech are indicated.

The various fissures and gyri are used to locate the lobes into which the cerebrum has been divided, and to describe various points thought to be related to specific sensory and motor activities. For example the *central sulcus* (fissure of Rolando) separates the *frontal* and *parietal* lobes. Between the central sulcus and the precentral sulcus is the precentral gyrus, an area thought to be involved in motor activity. The *lateral sulcus* (fissure of Sylvius) separates the temporal lobe below from the frontal and parietal above. There are five lobes in each hemisphere: namely, the frontal, parietal, temporal, occipital, and insula. The insula lies within the lateral fissure and is not visible on the surface. The lobes approximate closely the cranial bones listed in Table III.

The two hemispheres are united by bands of nerve fibers that cross the midline. The most prominent is *corpus callosum.*

A much used system for describing certain functional areas of the cerebrum was originated by Brodmann in 1909. Brodmann, using a numbering system, designated nine general functional areas which he divided into approximately fifty secondary areas. The original system has been expanded and currently includes more than 200 numbered areas. As an example, the principal motor area is usually described as being in the precentral convolution of the frontal lobe, just in front of the fissure of Rolando, in Brodmann's area 4.

If the cerebral hemispheres just discussed are cut into slices it will be observed that the surface or *cortex* in fresh brains is grayish in color; it is consequently called *gray matter.* Gray matter is composed largely of nerve cells. *White matter* is formed largely by processes or fibers of nerve cells.

The interior of the hemispheres is composed partly of white matter and partly by well-demarcated areas of gray matter called collectively the *basal nuclei* or *basal ganglia* which comprise the diencephalon to be discussed next.

The Diencephalon. The diencephalon (interbrain) lies between the cerebrum and the midbrain and, as we have just said, is comprised largely of gray matter called basal ganglia. Here, as well as in the midbrain, are centers which in cooperation with the cerebrum control voluntary muscles. The centers connect directly or indirectly with primary motor centers in the cerebrum above and project down into the midbrain. Since these nuclei are embedded in the base of the hemispheres, they are difficult to visualize.

The masses of gray matter in the diencephalon form a medial group including the *caudate nucleus, thalamus, hypothalamus* and the *subthalamic nucleus,* and a lateral group formed by the *lentiform nucleus* (composed of *putamen* and *globus pallidus*), and the *amygdaloid nuclei.* The medial and lateral groups are separated by a band of white matter called the *internal capsule.* Each internal capsule emerges eventually from the base of the cerebrum as a cerebral peduncle and delineates what is generally considered the midbrain. Nerve fibers in the internal capsule connecting the caudate and lentiform nucleus are arranged in parallel groups giving the area a striated appearance. Thus these structures are often collectively called the *corpus striatum,* and the bodies themselves, *striate bodies* (see Fig. 4).

Thalamus—the thalamus is a large ovoid structure situated at the base of the cerebrum. It is composed of two conspicuous nuclear masses separated by a deep, median cleft, the third ventricle, mentioned later. The thalamus is thought to be an important relay station where sensory pathways of the cord and brain stem form synapses on their ways to the cerebrum. The thalamus apparently acts as a center of primitive, uncritical sensation. Electrical sensation here causes a feeling that "something is happening" giving rise to exaggerated feelings of pleasure or pain. In the ventral portion of the thalamus are nuclei associated with afferent paths for special and general senses on their way to the cerebral cortex. The medial geniculate body, one of this group, is an important relay station for auditory sensations on their way to the temporal lobe.

Hypothalamus—the hypothalamus lies beneath the thalamus and forms the floor and part of the lateral wall of the third ventricle. It contains temperature-regulating centers and controls heat-loss functions such as sweating and panting; other centers for preventing heat loss by vasoconstriction and for increasing heat production by shivering are located in the posterior part. When not under

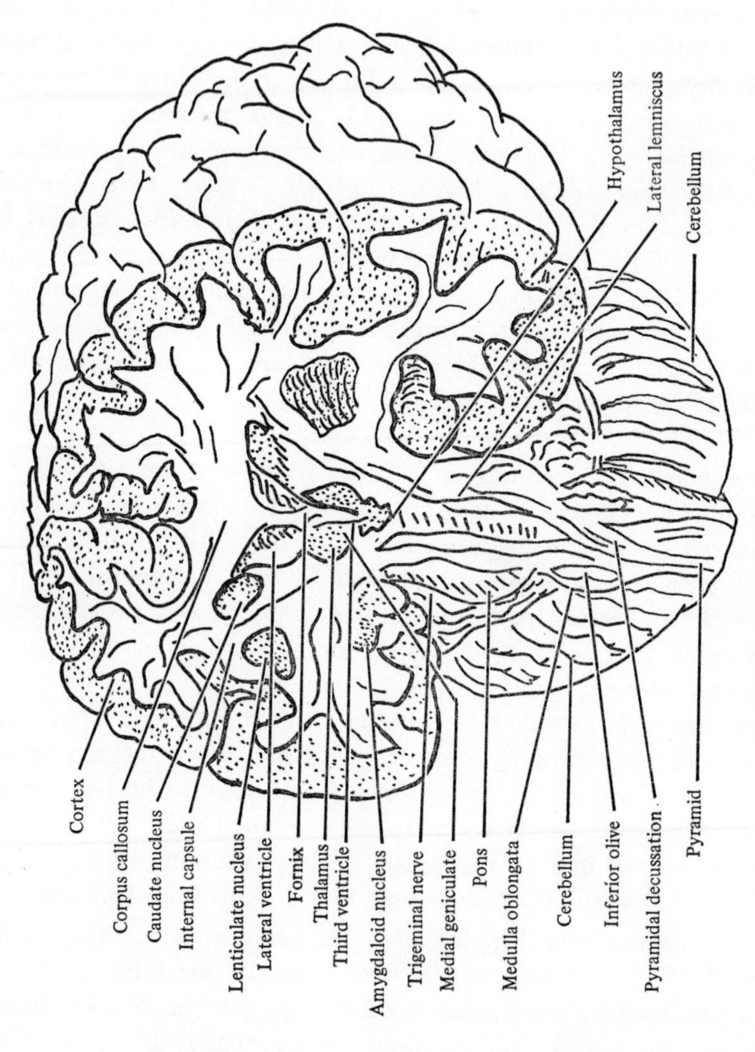

FIGURE 4. Frontal section of the brain.

control of the higher cerebral centers emotional manifestations are thought to initiate in the hypothalamus. It is thought that physiological manifestations of emotion are expressed through the hypothalamus.

Midbrain

The midbrain or *mesencephalon,* is formed by the two cerebral peduncles mentioned previously, containing nerve tracts connecting the cerebrum with the hindbrain and spinal cord. On the posterior surface of the midbrain are four rounded eminences, *corpora quadrigemina;* the upper two are the *superior colliculi* concerned with visual reflexes and the lower two or *inferior colliculi,* centers for auditory reflexes. Also located in the midbrain are the *red nucleus* and *substantia nigra* which connect with the corpus striatum and the premotor cortex. The cerebellum is thought to send many of its impulses to muscles via the red nucleus in the rubrospinal tract to be discussed later.

Hindbrain

The hindbrain is often divided into the *metencephalon* containing the *pons* and *cerebellum,* and the *mylencephalon* containing the *medulla.*

Pons—the pons contains gray matter and white fibers. It lies ventral to the cerebellum and forms a bridge between the midbrain and the medulla as well as between the halves of the cerebellum. Its dorsal portion is continuous with the reticular formation of the medulla. The pons forms an important connecting link between the motor control of activity initiated in the cerebellum and the higher motor centers in the cortex. Nuclei of the fifth, sixth, seventh and eighth cranial nerves are located in the pons.

Cerebellum—the cerebellum lies in the posterior cranial depression and is covered by a tentlike roof of dura mater, the *tentorium,* which separates it from the posterior part of the cerebrum. It is composed of a middle portion, the *vermis,* and two lateral hemispheres. The cerebellum is connected to the brain stem proper by three bands of fibers called peduncles. The superior peduncle connects with the midbrain; the middle passes through the pons across the midline to unite the cerebellar hemispheres; the inferior, containing fibers of the dorsal spinocerebellar tracts of the cord, connects with the medulla.

All activities of the cerebellum are thought to be below the level of consciousness functioning as reflex centers through which coordination and refinement of muscular movements are affected and by which changes in tone and strength of contraction are related to maintaining posture and equilibrium. *Ataxia,* one form of cerebral palsy, is thought to occur as a result of damage to the cerebellum.

Medulla—the medulla lies between the spinal cord and the pons, and its structure closely resembles the cord. All ascending and descending pathways of the cord are represented here. Some of the fiber tracts end here while others cross from side to side without interruption. In the medulla are the nuclei of the last four cranial nerves, C-IX to C-XII inclusive. In the medulla are such vital centers as the cardiac, vasomotor and respiratory.

The Spinal Cord

The spinal cord is the second major division of the central nervous system. It occupies the dorsal or vertebral cavity mentioned earlier (see Fig. 1). The cord is protected by the vertebrae, the irregularly shaped bones organized into one, long single column. There are seven cervical vertebrae in the neck region; twelve thoracic vertebrae in the chest; five lumbar vertebrae in the abdomen; one sacrum in the pelvis (originally five sacral vertebrae) and finally one coccyx composed of several segments. The names and location of the vertebrae are important to remember since they are landmarks for structures and nerves presented later (see Table III).

Each of the twenty-six vertebrae has a heavy body from which an arch extends backward enclosing a large opening called the vertebral foramen. These various foramina in turn form a continuous channel called the *vertebral column* or *canal* in which lies the spinal cord.

The spinal cord occupies the upper two thirds of the vertebral canal. Composed of thirty-one segments of nervous tissue, each has a pair of spinal nerves. (The spinal nerves will be discussed later in connection with the peripheral nervous system.)

The cord extends from the foramen magnum, where it is continuous with the medulla oblongata, to the level of the disc between the first and second lumbar vertebrae. Until the third month of fetal life, the cord extends the entire length of the canal; thereafter, however, because of the more rapid linear growth of the vertebral column, the cord appears to have been drawn upward within the canal. This disparity results in the nerves rooting in the lumbar and sacral regions passing for some distance in the canal before making their exits. Because of its appearance, it is called the *cauda equina.*

A transverse section at any level of the spinal cord shows the gray or nuclear matter to be internal and arranged like the letter H with a dorsal and ventral horn in each half of the cord. Each horn is cross-connected by a transverse gray band. In the exact center of this band is a central canal continuous with the brain ventricles. In many instances the central canal is totally obliterated at various levels.

The white matter in the more external area of the cord forms

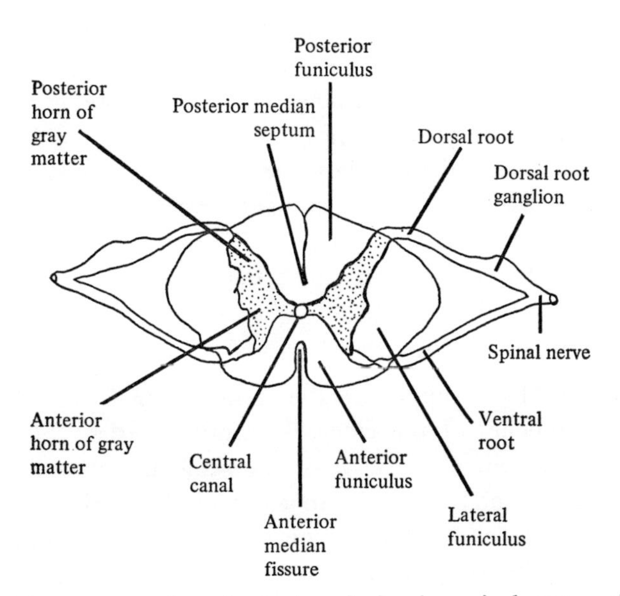

FIGURE 5. Transverse section of spinal cord, showing spinal roots and arrangement of white and gray matter. Note that a septum continues inward from the posterior median sulcus to divide the white matter into two posterior funiculi.

anterior, posterior and lateral columns, or *funiculi.* Within the various funiculi are ascending and descending tracts (sensory and motor) whose fibers have the same origin and ending; also present are *fasciculi* containing fibers belonging to two or more tracts (see Fig. 5).

The anterior columns forming the ventral or anterior projections of the letter H contain the ventral horn cells whose axons constitute the ventral root efferent (motor) fibers of the spinal nerve which innervate the muscles. The posterior or dorsal columns of the H contain afferent fibers branching into rami running in bundles or tracts to other levels of the cord or brain, or synapsing with internuncial neurons, or with ventral horn cells in the gray matter at the same level. The lateral columns of gray matter, most prominent in the thoracic region of the cord, contain cell bodies of axons which as preganglionic fibers pass to the sympathetic ganglia of the autonomic nervous system discussed later.

Blood Supply of the Brain

The blood supply of the cranial cavity is derived from two pairs of arteries in the neck, the *common carotid* and the *vertebral.* All vessels lie in the subarachnoid space before entering brain substance. After many branchings, the arteries form capillaries. The veins stemming from the capillaries return to the subarachnoid space after bathing the brain substance and eventually empty into the dural sinuses (spaces in dura mater). These in turn empty into the internal jugular veins through which the blood returns to the heart.

Blood Supply of the Meninges

The main blood supply of the dura mater is via the middle meningeal branches of the external carotid arteries. Each ascends through a foramen in the base of the skull and then lies between the dura mater and the skull. In cases of skull injury the arteries are sometimes torn resulting in bleeding called extradural hemorrhage—sometimes very serious because of consequent pressure on the brain.

Blood Supply of the Cord and Spinal Roots

An anterior spinal artery arises from each vertebral artery; the two join and form a single artery descending in the anterior medial fissure of the spinal cord. A posterior spinal artery also arises from each vertebral artery. Each then descends along the posterior aspect of the spinal cord and breaks up into plexiform channels in the lower part of the cord. Blood is returned by veins that generally follow the same route as the arteries.

Cerebrospinal Fluid

The fluid is clear and colorless and is produced by the choroid plexuses (tufts of small blood vessels in the lateral, third and fourth ventricles). The cerebrospinal fluid circulates from the lateral ventricles to the third ventricle then through the aqueduct of Sylvius into the fourth ventricle. (Ventricles are cavities within the brain—lateral ventricles are in the interior of each hemisphere; the third ventricle is in the diencephalon; the fourth, in the hindbrain between the cerebellum behind and the pons and medulla in front.) From the fourth ventricle the fluid moves into the subarachnoid space of the meninges via the median aperture—a thin membrane—in the fourth ventricle.

By thrusting a lumbar puncture needle between the third and fourth lumbar vertebrae into the subarachnoid space, the pressure of the cerebrospinal fluid can be measured by an attached manometer. Abnormal conditions—a tumor for example—by obstructing circulation may raise fluid pressure. The fluid may also be withdrawn and examined for bacteria, cells, or chemicals not normally present. The fluid that is withdrawn may be replaced by air or an opaque oil and detected by x-ray photography. The position of an obstructing mass may thus be determined. Anesthetics, such as procaine, may also be introduced into the fluid for spinal anesthesia.

Chapter 3

THE PERIPHERAL NERVOUS SYSTEM

THE BRAIN and the spinal cord just discussed are intimately related to the *cranial* and *spinal* nerves comprising the peripheral nervous system. Those nerves, it should be noted, arising from plexuses formed by spinal nerves are also called *peripheral* nerves. They are part of the total system but probably are understood better as special nerves. The *phrenic* and *sciatic* peripheral nerves, for example, emanate from the cervical and sacral plexuses respectively.

SPINAL NERVES

There are thirty-one pairs of spinal nerves corresponding to segments of the vertebral column. They are classified as eight cervical, twelve thoracic, five lumbar, five sacral and one coccygeal (see Fig. 6). Mentioned previously, the spinal nerves are formed by fibers from the dorsal and ventral roots in the posterior and anterior portions of the cord respectively which join as they pass out through the intervertebral foramen. Near or in each foramen is an ovid swelling of each dorsal root called the *spinal ganglion.* Since spinal nerves are composed of both dorsal (sensory) and ventral (motor) processes, all are *mixed* nerves carrying both sensory and motor impulses. The spinal nerves after leaving the intervertebral foramen continue for only a few millimeters before dividing into anterior and posterior branches.

Generally, the posterior divisions supply the muscles of the back and skin covering them. The larger anterior division forms the main part of the spinal nerves and supplies the muscles and skin of the extremities and the remaining areas of the trunk.

Plexuses

In all regions except the thoracic, the anterior divisions of the spinal nerves interconnect to form networks of nerves called plexuses: *cervical, brachial, lumbar* and *sacral.*

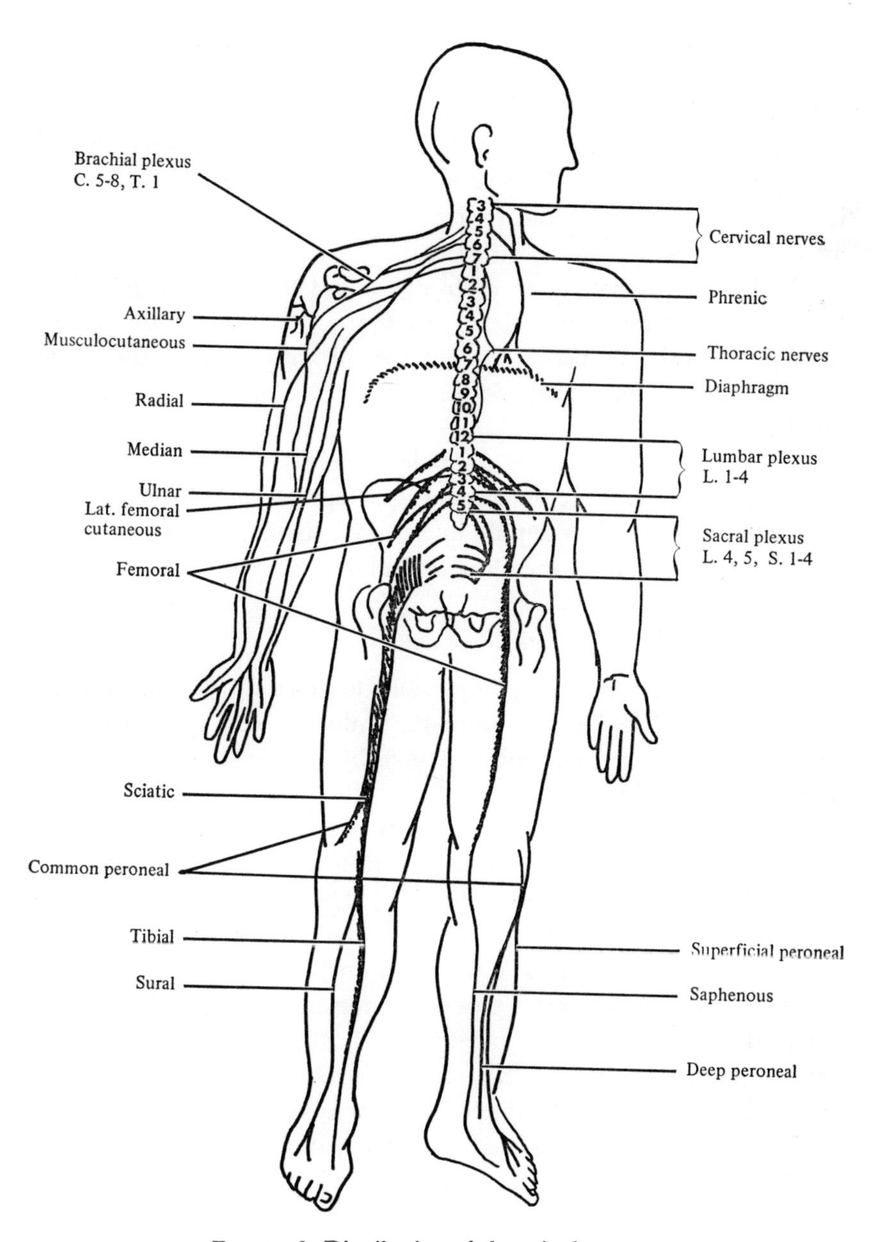

FIGURE 6. Distribution of the spinal nerves.

The cervical plexus is formed by the first four cervical nerves and supply structures in the neck region. An important peripheral or special nerve originating in the cervical plexus is the *phrenic* innervating the diaphragm.

The brachial plexus is formed from the fifth, sixth, seventh and eighth cervical and first thoracic nerves. Supplying upper extremities, important branches are the *radial, medial* and *ulnar,* nerves of the arm.

The lumbar plexus is formed from the last thoracic and first three lumbar nerves; the sacral plexus, from the fourth and fifth lumbar and the sacral. Branches from these plexuses supply the lower extremities. Its important nerves are the *obturator, femoral* and *sciatic.*

The spinal nerves in the thoracic area do not form a plexus. They pass out into the intercostal spaces, and are known as the *intercostal nerves.* They supply intercostal muscles, upper abdominal muscles and the skin of the chest and abdomen.

Reflex Activity of Spinal Cord

Although it is, normally, impossible to separate functionally the activity of the spinal nerves from the influence of higher centers in the brain, the nerve mechanism responsible for most activities of the organism is called reflex action.

A simple three-neuron type of reflex action may be illustrated as follows: A stimulus, for example an acid, applied to the skin affects the afferent neurons in the skin. The resulting nerve impulse is carried to a dorsal root in the spinal cord, thence through the dendrite, cell body, and axon of a neuron to the dendrite of a connecting neuron in the gray portion of the cord, where the impulse enters the ventral root of an efferent or motor neuron. From the axon of the motor neuron the impulse is carried into a spinal nerve connecting with a muscle which contracts in response to the impulse. Reflex actions of this kind are automatic, specific, and designed to perform a definite, useful function. Reflexes can become highly complex, involving multiple stimuli, many neuron pathways or arcs, and a number of responses. Some reflexes like chewing, swallowing, defecation, and crying, are instinctive or of extremely early development. Others, like walking, are learned from repeated experience.

Certain disorders of the nervous system obviously may be indicated by the failure of normal reflexes to function. Among the important reflexes often checked by physicians in diagnoses are the knee jerk or patellar reflex (leg extends in response to tapping the patellar tendon); the Achilles reflex (foot extends in response to tapping the tendon of Achilles); the corneal reflex (the eye closes in response to touching the cornea); the pupillar reflex (the pupil of the eye constricts in response to bright light); and the Babinski reflex (the toes extend in response to stroking the sole of the foot).

We have said previously that all spinal nerves carry both sensory and motor impulses. Let us look first at the sensory.

Ascending (Sensory, Afferent) Tracts

The successive connections in an ascending (afferent, sensory) pathway are referred to as *first order* neurons, *second order* neurons, etc. The first order neuron is associated with the receptor and organ.

Sense Receptors. Sense receptors are specialized nervous tissue classified according to their location and type of stimulus to which they respond. There are five major classifications of sense receptors: *Exteroceptive, interoceptive, proprioceptive, special,* and *mixed.*

Exteroceptive receptors, within the skin or body wall, are sensitive to touch, pressure, pain and temperature. *Interoceptive* receptors are contained within the smooth (involuntary muscles) glands and blood vessels and are related to all visceral behavior. *Proprioceptors* located in muscles, tendons, and joints are sensitive to position, movement, and tension. What is called the *stretch reflex* occurs when proprioceptors enable a muscle to respond adaptively to any force tending to stretch it or change its shape—a balance (muscular tonus) between agonists and antagonists, avoiding excessive tension or excessive relaxation, is thus maintained.

Special sensory receptors are related to audition, vision, taste, smell, and balance; *mixed* are related to sensations of itch and vibration.

Sensory Fibers. Impulses from sensory receptors enter the spinal cord via fibers in the dorsal roots in the cord. Many of these synapse with internuncial neurons in the gray matter of the cord. These in turn connect with motor neurons at various levels thus completing the spinal reflex arcs. Other secondary neurons receiving sensory activity in the cord ascend to the brain. Some important sensory fibers do not synapse on entering the cord, but ascend all the way to the medulla. Some of these fibers from receptors in the toes, for example, are very long. There are no motor fibers comparable for directness of communication.

The sensory fibers can be discussed in terms of the tracts in which they ascend. *Fasciculus gracilis* and *fasciculus cuneatus* are the two major efferent tracts making up the posterior funiculus or dorsal white columns (Fig. 5). They are fibers of first order neurons forming the first link in the pathway for sensations of position, movement, and touch-pressure. The terminal fibers of these tracts are in the medulla; from here they ascend in the final link to the cerebrum.

Ventral (Anterior) Spinothalamic Tracts—these tracts much like fasciculus gracilis and cuneatus convey impulses from proprioceptors. They are formed from fibers of second order neurons, ascend in the anterior funiculus, and terminate in the thalamus, from which they ascend finally to the cerebrum.

Dorsal Spinocerebellar Tracts—these tracts in the lateral funicule, are composed of second order neurons and receive impulses from proprioceptors. They ascend to the medulla and enter the cerebellum by the inferior cerebellar peduncle. Since the spinocerebellar fibers do not, apparently, actually reach the higher levels or what is called consciousness but go to the cerebellum, they are related to what might be called "unconscious muscle sense" since the cerebellum integrates and coordinates muscle activity. This type of behavior is illustrated in the stretch reflex mentioned earlier.

Lateral Spinothalamic Tracts—these tracts are composed of second order neurons constituting the second part of the pathway for pain and temperature. From the thalamus they ascend in a final chain to the cerebrum (Brodmann 1, 2, 3).

Only the major ascending sensory tracts have been presented here. Any standard text on neurology (see references) will provide a more comprehensive analysis. For the purposes of this text we believe a more detailed discussion is unnecessary.

Descending (Motor, Efferent) Tracts

In descending (motor, efferent) pathways the terms *upper* and *lower* motor neuron are used. The lower motor neuron is associated with the effector organ, while the upper motor neuron includes the cells of origin and any interconnecting neurons leading to the ventral horn cell, i.e., the cell body of the lower motor neurons. Since efferent or motor tracts have their cells of origin in the higher center and terminate in the ventral gray columns of the spinal cord, it may be helpful to study the motor pathways in terms of various floors or levels: the *spinal cord, reticular formation (brain stem) cerebellum, basal ganglia,* and the *cerebral cortex.*

The *spinal cord* gray matter represents the lowest level of organization. Many cells in this gray matter, exclusive of motor cells, are capable of certain types of organized activity. The degree of organization or coordination depends apparently upon the animal. The classical experimental decerebrated frog exhibits no spontaneous activity; however, it does show coordinated responses to many types of stimulation.

The *reticular formation* in the brain stem represents the next level. Here the mixture of gray and white matter contains innumerable cells and fibers related to many different functions. The axons of many of these cells descend to the spinal cord and are called reticulospinal fibers. Many cells in the reticular formation are important in control of muscular activity.

The *basal ganglia* and certain portions of the *cerebellum* (apparently necessary for coordinated movement) send descending fibers to the reticular formation, and represent a still higher level of control.

The highest level of control is the *cerebral cortex.* The regions of the cortex from which motor paths originate are called motor areas (Brodmann 4, 6) and are located primarily in the frontal lobes (precentral gyrus). The cortex contains large numbers of nerve cells, the bodies of which tend to be arranged in six layers. In motor areas the fifth layer is thick and contains *pyramidal cells.* The axons of these cells leave the cortex and enter the white matter of the hemispheres where they descend in the internal capsules. Impulses may reach motor cells responsible for the final action either by relaying in various subcortical levels, or by traveling in direct pathways to the brain stem and spinal cord.

Muscular Activity

Although various levels of control are involved in much of our activity, one cannot first think of movements to be performed in a particular activity and then initiate the nervous impulses causing them. On the contrary, most activity fits into complex, almost automatic patterns. Many of these activities are laboriously learned (walking) and only after years of constant practice does a special skill, for example, the execution of a smooth forehand drive in tennis, become almost automatic. It is interesting, however, that even a veteran tennis player may come apart at the seams if during an important match his opponent mentions how well he is hitting his forehand. He begins to think consciously about the movement and apparently disturbs the automatic activity operating. Thus, he inadvertently throws the entire system out of automatic temporal unity. Before what has happened can be recognized, he is hitting his forehands into the net or over the baseline while his opponent smiles knowingly.

At the various levels just described, where the ascending sensory tracts pass upward and end, originate the great descending motor tracts: *cerebrospinal (corticospinal), corticobulbar, rubrospinal, vestibulospinal,* and *reticulospinal.*

The two *corticospinal* tracts originating in Brodmann's area 4 are also called *pyramidal* tracts. They form the great motor pathways from the cerebral cortex carrying impulses for voluntary movement—mostly skilled, voluntary movements requiring participation of a small number of muscle groups. Just before entering the spinal cord, about four fifths of the fibers cross in the medulla. These crossed fibers, together with a lesser number of uncrossed fibers, form the large *lateral corticospinal* tracts; the remainder of uncrossed fibers pass downward to continue in the ventral funiculus as the *ventral corticospinal* tracts. The fibers of the ventral corticospinal tracts not crossing in the medulla do eventually cross at successive levels of the cord where they terminate. A very few, it is thought, do not cross at all. Fibers from both tracts end directly, or through intercalated neurons, on ventral horn cells. The lateral tracts supply muscles of the extremities; the ventral tracts carry motor impulses reaching muscles of the trunk.

The corticospinal tracts are called *pyramidal* because their descending fibers form what appear to be pyramids in the medulla. All the remaining motor tracts are called *extrapyramidal*. There are, however, some who believe the various tracts are so closely associated anatomically that a clear division into pyramidal and extrapyramidal systems is more academic than accurate. Noteworthy, however, is the etiology of various forms of cerebral palsy traditionally associated with lesions in either the pyramidal or the extrapyramidal systems.

The *rubrospinal* tract arises in the cells of the red nucleus of the midbrain. The fibers cross immediately and descend in the lateral funiculus to end in relation to motor cells in the anterior columns of the cord in the same manner as the corticospinal tracts. Since the red nucleus receives fibers from the cerebellum, this tract is thought to carry impulses of unconscious muscle coordination related to proprioceptive impulses.

The *vestibulospinal* tract has its origin in cells of the lateral vestibular nucleus of the medulla. The tract adjusts muscular movements to impulses received from the semicircular canals and assists in maintenance of muscle tone and balance.

The *corticobulbar* tract has fibers which begin to separate from the internal capsule and synapse with nuclei of cranial nerves (to be discussed) leading to the eye. The remainder of the corticobulbar fibers pass through the pons and cross into the medulla where they synapse with nuclei of cranial nerves related to many of the speech organs. This tract, therefore, is significant since it has control over much speech musculature.

Generally speaking, although there is controversy, it may be said of the motor tracts just discussed that corticospinal tracts seem to be associated primarily with excitation of muscle activity, or that pyramidal tracts are excitatory. Other tracts, generally speaking (extrapyramidal tracts), are largely associated with inhibiting and controlling total muscle activity to provide for muscular tonus and integration of response.

In reference to integration and control of muscle response mention should be made of diadochokinesis and the fact that muscle agonists are contracted while antagonists are relaxed. This alternating muscular activity is apparently a result of reciprocal innervation. Presumably, when a stimulus is sent to one muscle to contract an inhibitory stimulus is not sent to an antagonist muscle to relax. It is, rather, an inhibition of the transmission of the stimulus to the antagonist which causes decrease of tonus or relaxation. It is thought that in normal speech the inhibition is rapidly and efficiently shifted from one muscle group to another.

CRANIAL NERVES

The cranial nerves are the second major division of the peripheral nervous system. Cranial nerves are designated as those attached to the brain and passing out through the foramina of the skull. There are twelve pairs symmetrically arranged and distributed primarily to the structures of the head and neck. Because of the diversity of their function they have been given names as well as numbers (Roman). The numbers are based on the location or points of origin or insertion into the brain or brain stem. C-I (olfactory) is highest and most anterior; C-XII (hypoglossus) is lowermost having its source approximately at the juncture of the medulla and the spinal cord. Most of the cranials have both motor and sensory roots, but a few have sensory roots only. Cranials do not have dorsal and ventral roots like the spinals. The sensory components have their cell bodies in ganglia outside the brain; the motor are in nuclei within the brain. The general areas they supply are as follows.

C-I (Olfactory). This arises in the olfactory mucous membrane of the upper part of the nasal cavity and ends in the olfactory bulb. Running backward from the bulb, the olfactory tracts are directed to the base of each of the frontal lobes. This nerve is purely sensory.

C-II (Optic). Like the olfactory, the optic is purely sensory. It arises from the retina of the eye, runs posteriorly and forms, with the other optic nerve, the optic chiasma. Two bundles, the optic tracts, extend posteriorly around the cerebral peduncles and end near the superior colliculi in the mesencephalon. The fibers synapse in the thalamus with neurons conveying visual impulses to the occipital lobe. The optic nerves and tracts are thought not to be true peripheral nerves but fiber tracts of the central nervous system connecting the retina—a part of the CNS—and the brain.

C-III (Oculomotor). This nerve contains both sensory and motor fibers. Sensory fibers arise from all but two of the extrinsic eye muscles. Efferent fibers originating in the midbrain run anteriorly and end in muscles that attach to the eyeball and move it in various directions.

C-IV (Trochlear). The smallest of the cranials this nerve is mixed, supplying muscle sense and the impulse for movement to the superior oblique muscle of the eye. Like oculomotor, the efferent fibers have their origin in the midbrain from where they lead to the superior oblique muscle.

C-V (Trigeminal). Largest of the cranials, the trigeminal has a large sensory root and a smaller motor one. Both are attached to the side of the pons. Near the pons the sensory root has an enlargement, the trigeminal ganglion, from which three large branches arise. The *ophthalmic* branch sends fibers to the skin of the upper eyelid, side of the nose, forehead and anterior half of the scalp. It also supplies the lacrimal gland, cornea (pain) and the conjunctiva. The *maxillary* division conveys sensory impulses from the skin of the cheek, anterior temporal region, upper lip, upper teeth and mucous membrane of the nose. The *mandibular* division carries sensory impulses from the side of the head, chin, mucous membrane of the mouth, lower teeth and anterior two thirds of the tongue. The main trunk of trigeminal eventually passes into the pons (see Fig. 7).

The smaller motor root originates in the pons and runs along and becomes part of the trunk of the mandibular division of trigeminal. These fibers supply muscles of mastication, and are therefore of considerable importance in articulation of speech sounds for which the muscles of mastication are used extensively.

C-VI (Abducens). This mixed cranial nerve completes the innervation of the extrinsic muscles of the eye by supplying afferent and efferent fibers to the lateral rectus muscle attached to the eyeball providing for muscle sense and motion. Abducens arises in the pons, and afferent fibers also take the same route into the pons.

C-VII (Facial). The facial nerve consists of motor and sensory divisions. From the taste buds of the anterior portion of the tongue sensory fibers pass via the internal acoustic meatus to terminate in

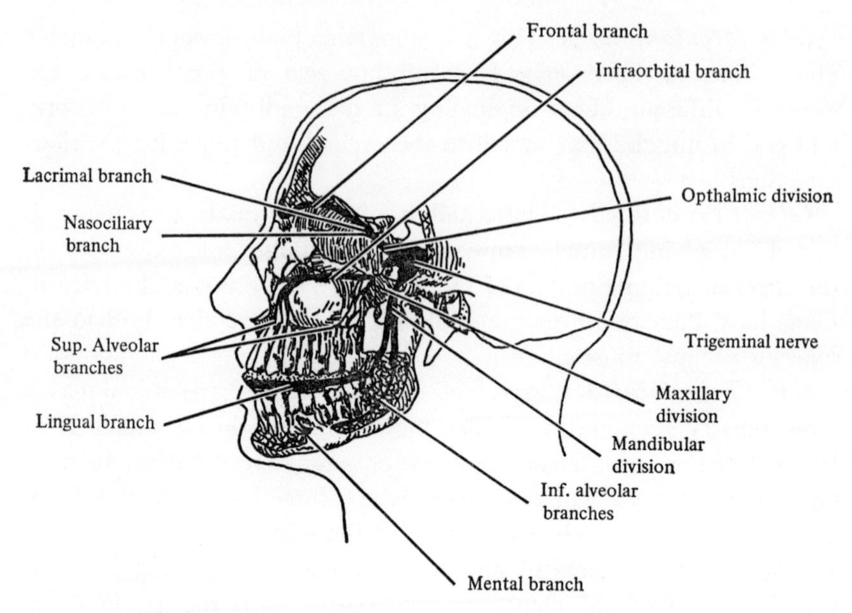

FIGURE 7. Distribution of the trigeminal nerve.

the medulla where they synapse with cells going to the cerebral cortex giving the sensation of taste.

The motor division of the facial arises in the lower part of the pons at its junction with the medulla. Portions of the motor fibers supply muscles of facial expression used in articulation of speech sounds.

C-VIII (Auditory). This has also been called *acoustic* and *vestibulocochlear*—a new term. There are two divisions of this nerve: *vestibular* and *cochlear*. Both are related to carrying sensory impulses from the inner ear. Afferent fibers of the cochlear nerve arise in the cochlea and pass to their cell bodies in the spiral ganglion near the cochlea. These axons then run through the internal acoustic meatus and terminate in the medulla. From the medulla they synapse with neurons along the auditory pathway (mentioned in detail later) to be perceived ultimately in the cortex.

Damage to the cochlear branch of C-VIII is, of course, related to hearing impairments usually classified as *perceptual* or *central.* Its importance to the speech process is obvious.

The vestibular nerve mediates the impulses for equilibration. Connections from it are made in the medulla with neurons in the vestibulospinal tract and with neurons relaying impulses to the cerebellum. This branch arises in fibers from the semicircular canals, utricle and saccule of the internal ear. After this branch enters the cranium via the internal acoustic meatus, it joins the cochlear branch to become one trunk.

C-IX (Glossopharyngeal). The glossopharyngeal nerve, via afferent fibers, provides for reflex control of the heart, taste and the swallowing reflex. Afferent neurons whose bodies are found in the jugular and petrosal ganglia enter the skull and pass into the medulla by way of the jugular foramen.

Efferent fibers to the muscles of the pharynx (swallowing) and the parotid gland (secretion) originate in cell bodies in the medulla.

C-X (Vagus). This nerve has the most extensive distribution of all since it goes to structures in the thorax and abdomen as well as in the head and neck. Afferent impulses are obtained from the mucous membrane of the larynx, trachea, lungs, bronchi, arch of the aorta, esophagus and stomach. Through this innervation the respiratory reflexes of coughing and sneezing, reflex inhibition of the heart rate, and sensations of hunger are facilitated. Sensory fibers run to their cell bodies in the jugular ganglion and thence to the medulla through the jugular foramen.

Cell bodies of the efferent fibers lie in the medulla. The various branches include meningeal, auricular, pharyngeal, superior laryngeal, superior and inferior cardiac, recurrent laryngeal, bronchial, esophageal, pericardial and abdominal. The vocal folds are innervated by the recurrent and superior laryngeal branches of Vagus (see Fig. 8).

C-XI (Spinal Accessory). The accessory consists of two parts, the bulbar and spinal divisions. Afferent and efferent components carry muscle sense and motor impulses for the muscles in the palate, sternocleidomastoidius and trapezius. All of these muscles are related to various aspects of speech production. Entering the skull through the jugular foramen, afferent fibers terminate, and efferent fibers arise, in the medulla.

C-XII (Hypoglossal). The hypoglossal nerve runs from the medulla dorsally to the vertebral artery through the hypoglossal foramen to the inferior surfaces of the tongue. Both muscle sense

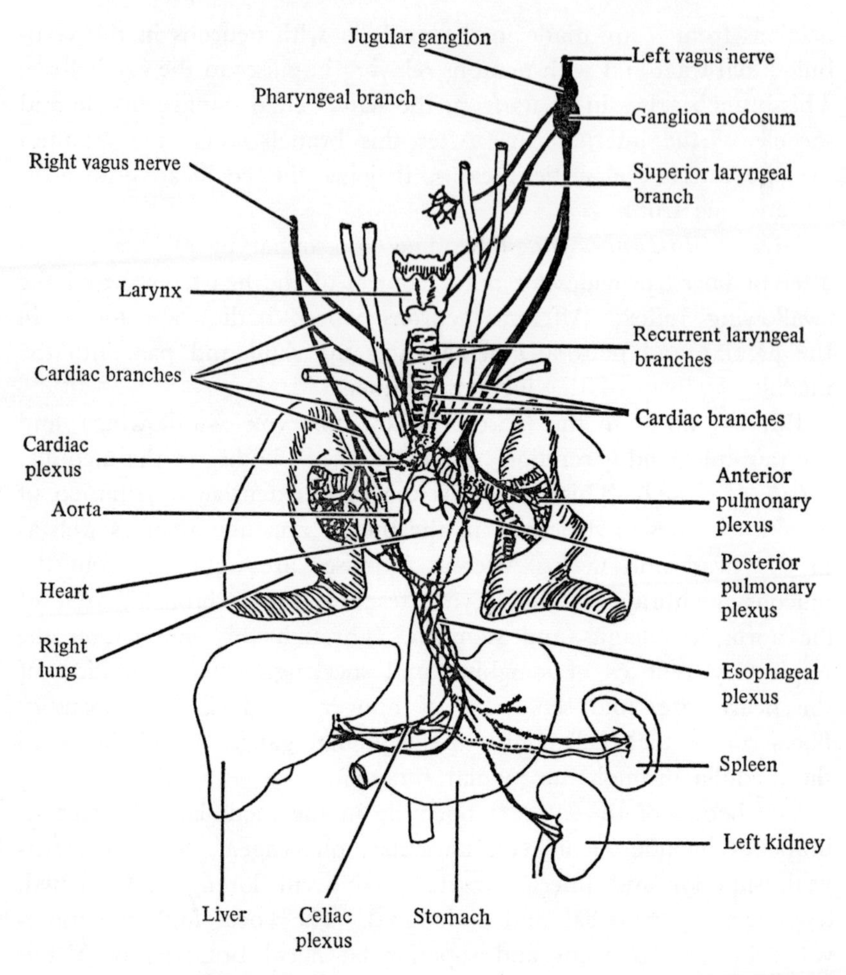

FIGURE 8. Distribution of the vagus nerve.

and motion are provided for the muscles of the tongue by this nerve. The importance of this nerve to the articulation of speech sounds is, of course, critical.

In summary, it should be noted which of the cranials are closely related to speech production. The following should receive special attention: C-V (trigeminal), C-VII (facial), C-VIII (auditory), C-IX (glossopharyngeal), C-X (vagus), C-XI (spinal accessory), and C-XII (hypoglossal).

Chapter 4

AUTONOMIC NERVOUS SYSTEM

ALTHOUGH THE next groups of nerves to be discussed are not truly "autonomic" by being structurally and/or functionally independent of other divisions of the nervous system, they are usually, largely for the sake of convenience, considered as a separate system.

The tissues of the body requiring autonomic innervation are supplied with nerve fibers arising from autonomic ganglion cells. These autonomic ganglia are of three types in the system: *vertebral ganglia, prevertebral ganglia* and *terminal ganglia.*

The vertebral ganglia are located on each side of and anterior to the cord in what is called the *sympathetic trunk* extending from the base of the skull to the coccyx in the form of a stepladder or paired chain of twenty-two ganglia. Each is cross-connected like the horizontal rung of a ladder. Each ganglion also extends fibers to the ganglia above and below like the vertical sides of a ladder. Delicate fibers, *rami communicantes,* connect each spinal nerve to a corresponding vertebral ganglion (see Fig. 9).

Some fibers concerned with the abdominal and pelvic viscera form plexuses. These plexuses have their own sympathetic ganglia. The various nerves forming the plexuses do not make contact with the vertebral ganglia, but pass through it. They are, therefore, called *prevertebral ganglia.* These plexuses have been given the names of *celaic, mesenteric, splanchnic, renal, phrenic,* and *aorticorenal.*

The *terminal ganglia* are upon or in the organs innervated by the autonomic system.

The fibers prior to making contact with the ganglia just mentioned are called *preganglionic.* They are located in the spinal cord and the brain stem. Those in the cord are in the lateral portion of the intermediate zone of the gray matter throughout the thoracic and the first two lumbar segments, and in the gray matter in the second, third and fourth sacral segments.

A. Eye
B. Lacrimal Gland
C. Respiratory Pas.
D. Submaxillary Gland
E. Sublingual Gland
F. Parotid Gland
G. Heart
H. Trachea
I. Bronchi, Lungs
J. Esophagus
K. Stomach
L. Liver
M. Pancreas
N. Intestines & Blood Vessels
O. Suprarenal Gland
P. Kidney
Q. Bladder
R. Reproductive Organs

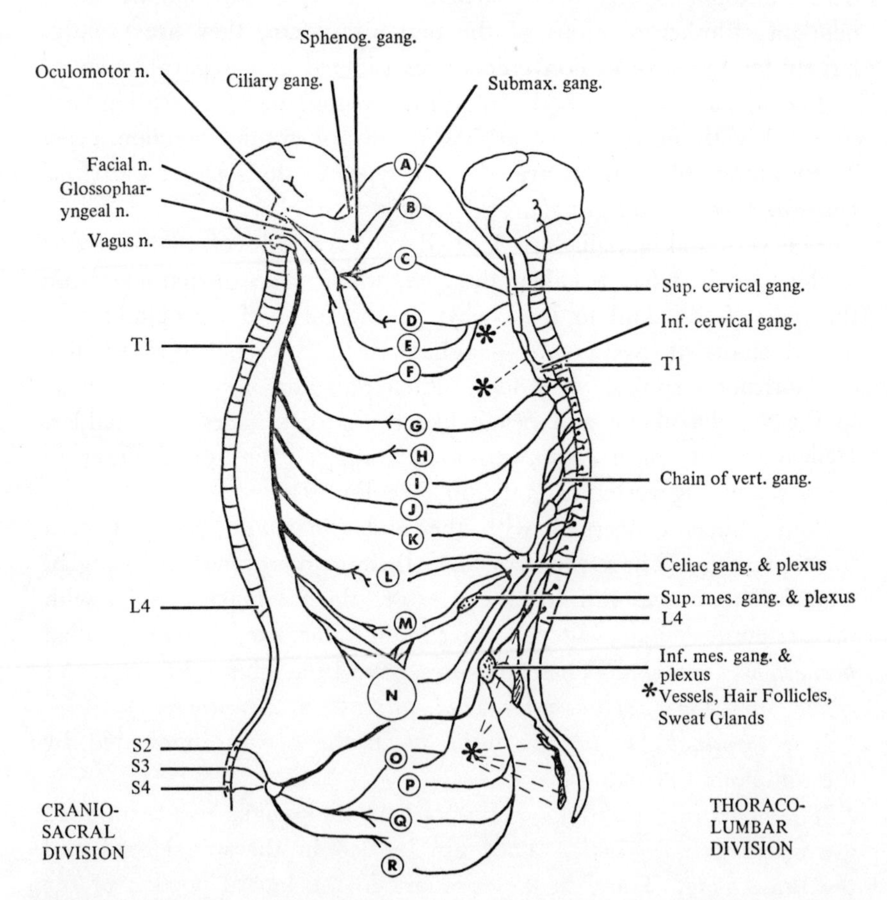

FIGURE 9. The autonomic nervous system. The craniosacral division is shown on the left, the thoracolumbar division on the right.

In the brain stem the preganglionics are aggregated in groups called nuclei and located, respectively, at the levels of the cranial nerve roots through which the preganglionic nerve emerges.

Divisions of the Autonomic System

The preganglionic fibers are found in only certain segmental levels of the spinal cord and brain stem. Some of the spinal, and some of the cranial, nerves include no preganglionic fibers. Preganglionics are present in C-III, C-VII, C-X, C-XI, all of the thoracic, L-1 and L-2, S-2, S-3, and S-4. The autonomic system thus may be said to contain a *cranial, thoracolumbar* and *sacral* divisions.

Sympathetic Division

The thoracolumbar levels constitute what is called the sympathetic division of the autonomic system. The preganglionic fibers emerging from the cord in the thoracic and first two lumbar nerves cross the ventral roots and the rami communicantes to contact the vertebral ganglia (sympathetic trunk). From here the axons of the vertebral ganglia cells travel in various directions. Some return to spinal nerves to reach blood vessels, sweat glands and smooth muscle fibers in skin. Others go directly to blood vessels and organs in the head, neck and thorax (these fibers are called *postganglionics*). Some of the preganglionics cross the vertebral ganglia without making contact there. Instead, they synapse with the prevertebral ganglia and their postganglionic fibers, then innervate viscera in the abdominal and pelvic areas via the splanchnic and other nerves.

Parasympathetic Division

The cranial and sacral divisions of the autonomic division comprise what is called the *parasympathetic* division. In the brain stem and the sacrum, the cranial and sacral nerve preganglionics do not join the vertebral ganglia (sympathetic) trunk, but extend through rami of the respective nerves into the terminal ganglia of the various organ effectors. Unlike the sympathetic division the terminal ganglia are not well defined in trunks, but are located variably in or near the various organs. Each preganglionic fiber synapses with relatively few cells; in some cases merely one cell. The postganglionic fibers supply fewer structures than the postganglionic sympathetic fibers.

Autonomic Functioning

Stimulation of autonomic ganglion cells or their axons causes liberation of chemical substances. The different kinds of substances released by the post ganglionic fibers of the sympathetic and parasympathetic divisions are generally thought to result in the functional differences in the two divisions. In both, the preganglionic fibers release a substance called acetylcholine (ACh). In the parasympathetic division, postganglionics also release ACh; however, in the sympathetic division, postganglionics release an adrenalin-like substance, sympathin. ACh is usually thought to be associated with inhibition (although it also may cause acceleration having a nicotine-like action), and adrenalin with excitement or acceleration.

In some instances the division is not as clear-cut as we have described it. Stimulation of some sympathetic ganglion cells, for example, results not in liberation of sympathin but in a substance very similar to ACh called parasympathin. Similarly, stimulation of some parasympathetic ganglion cells results in liberation, not of ACh, but of a substance very like sympathin. This suggests that neither the sympathetic nor the parasympathetic cells fall into clear-cut functional categories. To clarify the functioning of various cells and to avoid confusion of two divisions those cells liberating an adrenalin-like substance when stimulated have been classified *adrenergic;* those releasing an acetylcholine-like substance when stimulated, *cholinergic.*

Most body organs have a double autonomic innervation. For example, stimulation of the sympathetic cardiac nerves, which are adrenergic, causes acceleration of the heart rate, while stimulation of the parasympathetic cardiac nerves, which are cholinergic, results in retardation of the heart rate. Since what is usually described as "emotional behavior" is generally associated with autonomic activity, the individual who under most circumstances has balance between the two sets of impulses is therefore described as "emotionally stable." This is not to say, however, that adrenalin excess is never necessary.

In emergency circumstances rapid secretion of sympathin prepares the body for whatever may be happening, thus protecting it from complete inaction during the crisis.

Although it has not been clearly established, the hypothalamus is generally thought to be the cerebral control center for adrenergic stimuli. Less clear are the parasympathetic centers: some consider the reticular formation in the medulla and pons to be significant; others believe centers in the thalamus are important. In any event, higher centers, it should be noted, are operating in the total functioning of the autonomic system. One can experience this quite simply by recalling consciously a past event in which a great deal of anxiety or fear was experienced. By being aware of visceral sensations during this recall, autonomic reaction is experienced.

Generally speaking, adrenergic fibers are responsible for acceleration of heart beat, widening of pupils, constriction of blood vessels, inhibition of intestinal activity, secretion of adrenalin causing sugar rise and metabolic rate change, and emergency behavior. Cholinergic fibers are responsible for inhibition of the heart beat, constriction of pupils, vasodilation of blood vessels and lowering of the blood pressure, increase of salivary secretions (thus restoring digestive process), and for conserving, restoring, and calming.

ENDOCRINE GLANDS

The endocrine glands cannot be excluded from a discussion of the autonomic nervous system. Anatomically and functionally, as we shall see, the sympathetic (adrenergic) division of the autonomic system might be linked and called the *sympathoadrenal* system.

Although some few (pancreas) have both an external (duct) and internal (ductless) secretion, most of the endocrine glands, unlike the sweat glands for example, are ductless. They pour their secretions directly into the blood stream via blood vessels dividing from the glands. The secretions, called hormones or parahormones (not produced by living cells, e.g., glucose), pass to all parts of the body and may either produce or inhibit activity in areas far removed from the site of origin.

Hormones and parahormones do not initiate action themselves but energize the reactions catalyzed by specific enzymes. The action of particular glands may be independent or interdependent involving a very complex series of events. Generally, the endocrine system is adapted to the control of processes requiring slow, long-term adjustments. Thus they are related to growth, maturation, and control of the internal environment in metabolism.

The major endocrine glands are the *thyroid, parathyroids, pancreas, adrenals,* (suprarenals), *pituitary* (hypophysis) and *gonads.* The *thymus* gland in the neck and chest and the *pineal* gland in the cranium have not usually been included in discussions of the endocrine system because their function as endocrine glands has apparently not been established. However, the thymus it should be noted, has only recently been discovered to be the seedbed for the small white blood cells called lymphocytes critical to the body's ability to resist infections of all kinds. In addition, there is a thymic hormone apparently directly related to the establishment of the body's immunity system. Certain portions of the stomach and duodenum also have definite endocrine function, but these will not be discussed.

Thyroid Gland

The largest of the endocrine glands is located in the neck anterolateral to the trachea at its junction with the larynx. Two lateral lobes lie on either side of the trachea from the sixth tracheal cartilage to the thyroid and cricoid cartilages of the larynx. The isthmus connects the two lobes. The nerve supply consists of the parasympathetic branch of the superior laryngeal division of C-X (vagus) and sympathetic nerves from the cervical overflow of the thoracolumbar division. Of the various secretions of the thyroid gland the most functionally significant is *thyroxin* which contains approximately 65 per cent iodine. Thyroxin is directly related to body metabolism or the rate at which tissue changes as food materials are used for bodily use (anabolism) and energy is produced from breaking down tissue into waste material (catabolism).

Malfunctioning of the thyroid gland is not uncommon. A *hyperthyroid* individual may have protruding eyes, jitteriness, be uncomfortable in a cool room and perspire. He may eat large amounts, but gain little or no weight. His heart may beat abnormally fast, he may have insomnia and be unable to relax during the most tranquil circumstances. In *hypothyroidism,* the thyroid gland may greatly enlarge in an effort to compensate for the deficiency. In an adult the condition is called *myxedema* and the symptoms include obesity, sluggishness, chronic fatigue, dry skin, coarse hair, impaired circulation and, in some instances, a form of psychosis. In children, chronic hypothyroidism is called *cretinism.* These symptoms include mental retardation, small stature, and retardation in sexual development.

Parathyroid Glands

The smallest of the endocrines consist of four small bodies lying on the posterior surface of the thyroid gland. The parathyroid secrete *parathormone,* thought to be related to calcium and phosphorus metabolism. Marked deficiency in parathormone lowers blood serum calcium and elevates blood serum phosphorus and may result in a condition called tetany characterized by tonic spasms of the skeletal musculature and increased irritability of central and peripheral nerves. A slight deficiency of parathormone may result in improper development of teeth and bones. An excess may result in calcium in the intestines, kidneys and heart; a hyposensitivity of the nervous system, and demineralization and distortion of the skeletal system.

Pancreas

The pancreas lies on the posterior abdominal wall behind and below the stomach. Thoracolumbar nerve fibers extend to the pancreas through the celiac plexus; branches of vagus represent craniosacral innervation. The principle hormone of the pancreas is *insulin* which is essential to normal carbohydrate metabolism. Without normal amounts of insulin a condition called diabetes results. Unless properly treated this condition will cause death. Excessive insulin will cause fatigue, irritability, hunger and, in extremes, coma and death.

Adrenal (Suprarenal) Glands

The two adrenal glands are pyramidal structures located at the superior peaks of the kidneys. The glands are composed of an outer portion, the *cortex,* and an inner portion, the *medulla.* The medulla contains cells identical with the ganglion cells of the sympathetic division of the autonomic system. The medulla is innervated only by preganglionic fibers from splanchnic nerves; however, its secreting cells are structurally identical to postganglionic fibers of the sympathetic division. The close relationship between these glands and the sympathetic division should be noted.

The secretion of the medulla is called *epinephrine* or *adrenalin.* Adrenalin acts upon all structures of the body innervated by the thoracolumbar division of the autonomic nervous system with the exception of the sweat glands. Its effects are a rise in arterial blood pressure, constriction of the arteries (primarily in the skin and viscera), increased strength and rate of heart beat, inhibition of gastrointestinal musculature with the exception of the sphincters, relaxation of other smooth muscles, dilation of the pupil of the eye, relaxation of constriction of uterine muscle, liberation of glucose from glycogen stores of the liver, elevating blood sugar, and increase of the metabolic rate. The action just described is very similar to a description of the action of the sympathetic division of the autonomic nervous system.

The cortex has approximately twenty-eight hormones called *steroids.* All have the same basic structural nucleus as cholesterol, and are chemically related to the sex hormones. Various "steroids" are used commercially in beautification creams and lotions. The products, however, have had questionable approval.

Unlike the medulla, the cortex is essential to life. The total effect of adrenal cortex hormones include changes in growth (secondary sex characteristics), weight, basal metabolism, reproduction, neuromuscular activity, gastrointestinal function and body fluid balance. Interaction occurs among the adrenal cortex, the anterior lobe of the pituitary, the thyroid glands and the gonads.

Pituitary Gland (Hypophysis Cerebri)

This tiny gland, about the size of a pea, lies in the sphenoid bone in the floor of the skull. It is composed of three parts: *anterior, intermediate,* and *posterior.* The *anterior lobe* of the pituitary, often referred to as the master gland, controls other endocrine glands as well as bodily processes by several hormones. Among others, the following are most significant.

The *somatotropic* or *growth hormone* influences normal growth. If in early life there is deficiency, dwarfism results. Hyperpituitary may cause giantism in youth, while in an adult, excessive bone thickening, swelling, and deformation called *acromegaly* may result. Frequently, the mandible, bones of the skull and musculature used for oral speech (tongue, hyoid bone, larynx, vocal folds) are affected.

The *thyrotropic* hormone (TSH) is responsible for gross size and vascularity of the thyroid gland and consequently for its ability to function physiologically.

The *adrenocorticotropic* hormone (ACTH) affects the cortex of the adrenal gland much like the thyroid is affected and causes an increase in the production of adrenal cortex hormones.

The *gonadotropic* hormones are essential to normal sexual development, to maintenance of sexual characteristics and to reproducing characteristics of both sexes. Deficiency of this hormone may result in opposite sex speech behavior.

The *intermediate lobe* secretes a hormone regulating skin pigmentation.

The *posterior lobe* portion of the pituitary is connected via nerve tracts to the hypothalamus. It forms substances which act to constrict the smooth muscle of blood vessels (vasoconstriction) and to decrease the formation of urine by increasing resorption of fluid and the output of salt.

Gonads

In the male, sex hormones are derived in the gonads from the cells of the testis under the influence of the pituitary. *Testosterone* is said to be the true testis hormone. Normal secretion of testosterone is necessary for secondary sex characteristics to appear, for the stimulation of spermatogenesis, and the development of reproductive organs.

In females, the sex hormones are produced by the ovaries, but again under the influence of the pituitary. These hormones are related to growth, secondary sex characteristics, menstrual and ovarian cycles, implantation of the ovum in the uterus and development of placenta and the growth of, and milk secretion in, the mammary glands.

Disorders of the gonads in both sexes obviously result in many changes and consequent problems of adjustment.

Chapter 5

THE NEUROPHYSIOLOGY OF SPEECH

THE TITLE OF this chapter may strike some as presumptuous for it implies enough knowledge of neurophysiology to chart the true course of speech. Such, unfortunately, is not the case. What can be said, however, is that a great deal more is known about the neural processes involved in oral speech than was known ten years ago. The work of Doctors Penfield and Roberts and their associates at McGill University must be given major credit for this. Others (Kephart, 1960; Delacato, 1963), basing conclusions on observations of hundreds of clinical cases involving defective neurology in one form or another, have formulated hypotheses of neurological developmental learning (including speech) which have yet to be disproven.

When one considers the debates which have raged for years in attempts to explain "learning" (Hebb, 1949) it should be obvious why neurological speech processes will probably be debated for many, many years to come. For, as Penfield says,

> It is an astonishingly complex process that any speaker sets in motion. Consideration of it brings us, at once, face to face with the baffling problem of the nature of the physical basis of the mind. . . . I begin with what is called a thought. A succession of nerve impulses then flows out from my brain along the nerves in such a pattern that the appropriate muscles contract while others relax, and I speak. An idea has found expression in electrical energy, movement, vibrations in the air. The boundary which separates philosophy from neurophysiology and physics has been crossed.

But we are not finished, for

> When that sound reaches your (the listener's) ear drums, it is converted again into nerve impulses conducted along your auditory nerves and into your brain. The stream of nerve impulses results in a secondary mental proposition resembling, but far from being identical with, that of the speaker. It is a new perception. Again that strange, brain-mind frontier has been crossed—crossed twice by each utterance! (Penfield and Roberts, 1959)

What Penfield has suggested, and what becomes immediately apparent, is that when we attempt to analyze the speech processes at the neurological level we are entering a territory embracing not only the physical and biological sciences, but also philosophy, religion and psychology. The physical and physiological processes involved in speech behavior can be considered with far less difficulty (although they are numerous enough) than the psychic or thought processes. The dualists, for example, believe there is in each individual, in addition to the body and its living energy, a conscious spirit or soul which is the active accompaniment of brain activity, and is present from birth to death. This spirit, it is also believed by some, continues its existence after death of the body and is one with God.

It cannot, of course, be the purpose of this chapter to consider the validity of religious and philosophical arguments for a brain-spirit relationship. Most religions, it is generally agreed, are based on faith, and there seems to be little or no need for faith if there is reason. Thus, to rationalize a brain-spirit concept is to destroy one's faith in it. What we, therefore, propose to do in this chapter is to discuss neural processes thought to be involved in speech without questioning the possibility of spiritual activity.

In previous chapters we have named the various parts of the brain and discussed both sensory and motor pathways. It would be satisfying now if we could utilize this information by formulating a very orderly and precise outline labeled, "The Neural Speech Mechanisms." To some extent this is possible; however, in a much larger sense, it is not.

Sensory and motor impulses constantly being received and processed by the individual cannot, except for simple reflexive patterns, be isolated and inspected. Thus, we cannot generally speak of sensory perceptions A, B, and C and their exact relationship to motor responses A, B, and C with any degree of validity. Behavior, especially speech behavior, is rarely that simple. Instead we must think in terms of highly intricate combinations of numerous sensory-motor processes in relationship to behavior. Kephart roots his rationale for the education of brain-damaged children in what he calls *sensory-motor learning* (Kephart, 1960). Both, he contends, must be considered as a unit.

Although, as we shall see a bit later on, there are areas of the cerebrum assuredly related to speech processes, they can never be isolated since each is a part of a complex machine involving all levels of the central nervous system, much of the peripheral, and the two autonomic divisions.

ONTOGENY OF NEUROPHYSIOLOGY

Only as man has developed the structures (phylogeny) has he been able to utilize them for his own advancement. Thus ontogeny recapitulates phylogeny. The ontogenetic development of man in terms of neurophysiological organization and structure has been presented by Delacato (Delacato, 1963). A consideration of his proposal is, we believe, a logical starting point for a discussion of the neurophysiology of speech.

The progression of neurological organization proceeds vertically to the cortex as myelenization takes place. The various stages are chronologically predictable, and, significantly, prerequisite, according to Delacato, to normal development of hemisphere dominance and the consequent acquisition of communication skills—reading and speaking. The various neurological levels are discussed in the following paragraphs.

Gestation, Birth to 16 Weeks (Spinal Cord and Medulla)

During this period neurological organization occurs at the spinal cord and medulla. Primitive reflexes (muscle tone, reflex movement, preservation of life) are present *in utero*. At birth, the medulla controls vital functions like cardiovascular activity, gastrointestinal activity and breathing reflexes. Mobility is undulating and fish-like. There is movement, but no mobility; all is reflexive, including all vocalized behavior (crying). All the reflex activities require relatively short and uncomplicated neural pathways.

16 Weeks to Six Months (Pons)

During this period the child develops neurologically to the level of the pons. Both visual and auditory pathways cross the midline in the pons. It should be noted, however, that not all fibers cross.

The physiological base of the tonic neck reflex is in the pons. This reflex should be partially established prior to birth and tends to cease at about twenty weeks of age. The first use of the tonic neck reflex takes place intrauterinely. As the head turns, the arm and leg on the side toward which the head is turned will flex. Obstetrical procedures make use of the tonic neck reflex during the birth process to facilitate delivery. If this reflex is not present at birth some mechanism has, apparently, been neurologically impaired or underdeveloped prior to birth.

Delacato believes each level of neurological organization must have adequate opportunity to express itself in appropriate movements to insure normal neurological developmental learning. Thus, he cautions against merely placing a child on its stomach or permitting it to roll over without posturalizing the body in the proper tonic neck position.

The earliest mobility of the infant, it should be noted, is *crawling* during which the tonic neck reflex is used functionally to drag the body along. The movements, homolateral and typical of the amphibian (salamander, frog) have the arm and leg on the same side of the body flexed and the arm and leg on the opposite side of the body extended. Children, apparently, who are well-organized neurologically at the level of the pons sleep on their stomachs in a homolateral position typical of the tonic neck reflex. Thus, if the child lies on his stomach with his head turned to the left (right cheek touching the pillow) his left arm and leg will be flexed and his right arm and leg will be extended. The position is reversed if the head is turned to the right. Once sidedness has been established, right-sided individuals tend to sleep in the position described above; left-sided individuals in the reverse position.

Vision during this period is bi-ocular; the eyes are used alternately and rarely in concert. The eyes appear to be slightly crossed or to have what is called *strabismus*. Auditorily, there is recognition of gross sounds, but no ability to locate these sounds in space or to determine their distance.

Six Months—One Year (Midbrain)

At about six months, the child moves into the midbrain (mesencephalon) stage of development. The midbrain is composed primarily of the superior and inferior colliculi (corpora quadrigeminia) dorsally and the cerebral peduncles ventrally. The unusual abundance here of sensory nerves supplying the occular muscles, as well as their very close connection with the retinal fibers thought to be related to posture, are postulated as strong indices of the integration of posture, mobility and vision at the midbrain level.

At the midbrain level, the child learns to creep. He now moves in a cross-pattern fashion with his stomach no longer in contact with the floor. During creeping, it can be noted, the homolateral movement of arms and legs, present earlier, has now been replaced by a crossed pattern—the right hand and left knee make contact with the floor at the same time, and on the next propulsion, the left hand and the right knee make contact with the floor. In each instance the head is turned toward the forward hand. For the first time, apparently, the child has begun to use both sides of his body together in an organized way. The same neurological developmental growth can be observed in both vision and audition. Both eyes are now used in concert. They both begin to look at the same object in space simultaneously. The child is now binocular. Auditorily, the child now begins to locate sounds in space; he has some beginning awareness of their distance. He becomes binaural.

Vocal play now replaces the cooing, gurgling and grunting sounds, usually called babbling, evident in the previous period. During this period the child will produce every type of speech sound present in the English or any other language. The child seems to enjoy the process as he literally plays with sounds and sound combinations in a vast array of changing patterns. The listening bath is apparently necessary for the development of binaurality.

One Year—18 Months (Cerebral Cortex)

At about one year the child moves into early cortical function. (The cerebral hemispheres and their topography were discussed in Chap. 2).

During this period the child begins to acquire two very important foundations for later development: walking and talking. Since both are highly complicated neurological functions (compared to those previously learned) each is usually acquired separately. Thus, if the child has been engaged in vocal play activity, he will very often cease vocalizing entirely until he has gained some skill in walking.

As the child begins to pull himself up on the side of his crib, he begins his first attempts at being a biped. His early steps are quite awkward since he uses his hands not in the cross-pattern walking position typical of the older child, but held above his head or at the side, apparently as a kind of rudder. As walking becomes more proficient, it becomes more bilateral. Normally by age three or four, the child is walking cross-pattern utilizing both arms and legs for balance.

During this period the child continues with a more and more refined type of vocal play resembling true speech in form if not in meaning. His vocalizations are usually called *jargon.* He also begins now to echo the sounds he makes as well as the sounds in his environment. This suggests that a cortical awareness of sound has developed and that discrimination has occurred. Whether there is an essential fusion of auditory stimuli at this level comparable to visual stimuli is uncertain since a great deal about auditory perception remains unclear; however, although both ears do work together to some extent it seems unlikely the fusion is comparable to that necessary for visual perception.

During this period, according to Delacato, in addition to learning the sound combinations for various objects and ideas in his world, the child develops a growing fondness for music. At the outset this is a bilateral experience; however, later, as laterality and hemisphere dominance are established, music and tonality in general are relegated to the subdominant hemisphere. The skills of sound reception and production necessary for human speech become the province of the dominant cortical hemisphere. Recent research (Milner, 1962; Kimura, 1963) support this proposition. Thus, the skilled ear is the one chosen to listen to the tick of a watch or for comprehension.

By eighteen months the well-organized child is bilateral, binocular, and binaural. Those who are not, according to Delacato, have been restricted during the first year or pushed too fast. They have not, apparently, had sufficient opportunity to creep—a function in which, apparently, roots all the important development of both binocularity and binaurality.

Delacato, on the basis of his clinical experience, believes many children seen in speech clinics with articulation defects actually are poorly developed in binaural skills and consequently are unable to cope with speech sound differences. That speech sound discrimination is poor in many of these children has been demonstrated by research (Kronvall and Diehl, 1958; Diehl and Cohen, 1963). To what extent, however, this skill is related to binaurality is unknown.

Three Years—Eight Years

After the child has continued at the bilateral level of neurological organization for approximately two years, he moves into the next stage of neurological development—*laterality* which is unique in man. Up to this point, both hemispheres have been operating in concert. Now, however, the two hemispheres begin to take on separate functions—one becoming dominant, the other subdominant.

On the basis of a study of aborigines in which 108 of a total group of 114 were right-handed it could be concluded that right lateral dominance is not a mere product of our culture, but is of a universal nature. In our culture, estimations have shown 85 per cent to 95 per cent of the population to be right-handed. For those who are left-handed, there appears to be a genetic factor operating, or, as some have speculated, a lack of neurological development.

Sidedness, it should be noted, is far more important than handedness. Sidedness refers to the use of the arm, leg, eye, and ear all on the same side. The neurologically well-organized individual should by the age of eight have developed hemisphere dominance. If the left hemisphere has taken charge, there will be right-handedness, right-footedness, right-eyedness, and right-earedness in the sense that the right side will do the leading whenever there is a choice, and providing, of course, there is no organic injury to the right arm, leg, eye, or ear.

Since oral speech production requires the activation of many muscles, hemisphere dominance, it is logical to assume, must be established to insure organized temporal innervation of the speech musculature. The matter of dominance, however logical the arguments may seem, has never been clearly established.

In 1861, a French surgeon, Paul Broca, published a paper in which he described two patients who had lost speech as a result of lesions in the posterior part of the left, frontal convolution. At the time he proposed this area as being critical for speech. Consequently the third, left frontal convolution was called the "speech center" or "Broca's area" (see Fig. 3).

In 1874, Dr. Wernicke published a monograph in which he separated the general auditory area from what he called the "auditory speech area" located in the first, temporal convolution (Brodmann 41, 42). A lesion in this area, Wernicke was convinced, would produce loss of understanding of speech, or what is often referred to as *perceptual* or *receptive aphasia.* Wernicke did not, however, indicate this area to be only on the left side. Since only approximately half of the auditory fibers leading to the temporal lobe cross to the opposite hemisphere the argument for a single auditory center in either the right or left hemisphere becomes less tenable. This does not, however, preempt the belief that either the right or left auditory center may become functionally dominant for certain auditory perceptions.

The relationship of sidedness, hemisphere dominance, and a speech center will very probably be clarified as neurophysiology continues to be explored. In the meantime, empirical evidence seems to support the argument for a speech center in the left hemisphere. In the overwhelming majority of cases where there is paralysis along with aphasia, the paralysis is on the right side. (In almost 100 years only approximately 140 cases with aphasia and involvement of only the right hemisphere have been reported.) The clinical picture suggests that, since there is right paralysis in the majority of aphasia cases, neurological injury is in the left hemisphere and that a "speech center" therefore also exists in the left hemisphere. It is rare for a patient to have both left-sided paralysis and aphasia no matter what his handedness was prior to the cerebral injury.

Probably, the most conclusive evidence to support the argument that the left hemisphere contains a "speech center" has been presented by Penfield and Roberts (Penfield and Roberts, 1959). By applying electric current directly to the exposed cortex by means of craniotomy as a preliminary and precautionary procedure before excising cerebral tissue to relieve epilepsy, Penfield and Roberts were able to make several important conclusions regarding speech areas.

Upon electrical stimulation of the cortex two effects upon speech were produced—a positive one, stimulation; and a negative one, interference. When the current is applied to the motor area (Brodmann 4, 6) of either hemisphere, it may stimulate, producing speech, or it may interfere, causing a disorder of the motor control of the speech organs. In addition to the motor areas, it was discovered upon stimulation of Broca's area in the left hemisphere and the left posterior temporoparietal area (posterior parts of the second and third temporal convolutions, the supramarginal gyrus and the angular gyrus) that the following alterations in communication are produced: arrest, hesitation, slurring, repetition, distortion; confusion in numbers while counting; inability to name with retained ability to speak; misnaming with or without evidence of preseveration; difficulty in reading, and difficulty in writing. No vocalization, it should be noted, was produced by stimulating these areas—only the motor areas in both hemispheres produced vocalization by stimulation. Rarely were similar responses produced by stimulating the corresponding areas in the right hemisphere.

Penfield and Roberts concluded generally,

> From the standpoint of cerebral dominance the data from electrical interference support the conclusion . . . the left hemisphere is usually dominant for speech regardless of the handedness of the individual, with the exclusion of those who have cerebral injuries early in life. (Penfield and Roberts, 1959)

If, as has been reported, the left hemisphere usually contains the dominant speech areas regardless of handedness (except for a comparatively few cases) a strong, logical argument could be made for encouraging right-sidedness in all individuals with ambidexterity. Unfortunately, the actual evidence in this respect does not support such a simplified assumption.

In some individuals, for example, there may be a native predisposition for having speech represented either bilaterally or in the right hemisphere. The tendency for left-handedness and ambidexterity to be a familial characteristic supports the argument that genetic factors are at least to some extent related to sidedness. Krynauw (1950) and others have reported complete removal of a hemisphere diseased from early life without disturbance in speech. Hillier (1954) reported return of speech following excision of the left hemisphere in a teenager.

It appears logical to suspect that at least a small percentage of the population, because of genetic factors, inherit a propensity for right hemisphere dominance, including speech. Many of these, perhaps, since we live in a right-handed culture have difficulty adjusting to their native left-sidedness and develop, consequently, ambilaterality.

Another group, it could be argued, with native right-sidedness because of some minor brain damage in the left hemisphere at birth or very early in life, have compromised to the ambidextrous stage.

Although the picture is anything but clear, it appears logical, when feasible, to encourage one-sidedness in young children, and preferably right-sidedness if there is a choice. However, if one-sidedness is strongly resisted or appears difficult to achieve it may very well suggest a minor brain damage in one hemisphere necessitating the permanent use of the opposite hemisphere for the execution of some, but not all, activities. In such cases, ambidextrous behavior may very well be the most efficient (although not the most organized) behavior for the individual. For such cases, if difficulty in learning communication skills exists, one might ask whether achievement levels in these skills should be lowered. Perhaps, in some cases, by blaming the student's attitude rather than his unfortunate neurology for his below par performance, we are merely creating new problems rather than solving old ones.

The matter of whether stuttering behavior is directly or indirectly related to confused laterality or a shift in handedness (from left to right) has never been settled. In the late 1930's and early 1940's when the lateral dominance theory was widely accepted, individuals who had been shifted from left to right and who also stuttered were treated in speech clinics by having the native or left hand restored to what, apparently, was to have been its natural use in writing and other activities. In many instances the shift back appeared to reduce the stuttering behavior; in others, however, no change seemed apparent in the speech behavior. With the eventual development of personality inventories the pendulum swung sharply to the psychological side where it has remained.

Data reported by Heltman (1940) are of interest. In 1939 all entering students at Syracuse University were checked for laterality. Of 1,594 students, 216 were found who were either left-handed, ambidextrous, had been shifted from left to right, or who stuttered. The breakdown among these groups was as follows:

1,422 right-handed	15 stutterers	1.1% of r. h. group
34 left-handed	1 stutterer	2.9% of l. h. group
138 ambidextrous	4 stutterers	2.9% of ambidextrous group
77 shifted for writing	1 stutterer	1.3% of shifted group

On the basis of the data, since only one of the seventy-seven shifted from left to right stuttered, there appears to be little hazard in making such a shift. Further, since 2.9 per cent of the ambidextrous group stuttered as compared with 1.3 per cent of the shifted group (twice as many) it appears that a shift to right-handedness might actually be advisable for ambidextrous individuals as a therapeutic or preventive measure.

Unfortunately, a great deal of the current difficulty surrounding the etiology of, and therapy for, stuttering behavior stems from a lack of proper definition. Certainly, all are not talking about the same speech behavior when various investigations of stuttering are reported in the literature—there is too much discrepancy to conclude otherwise. What appears to have happened is for some to think of stuttering as the initial hesitation or stoppage in the flow of speech; while others think of stuttering as the associated symptoms (facial grimaces, accessory movements, etc.) resulting from the initial stop. Both may have different etiologies—the former a neurological one, the latter, a psychological one.

Before we leave the matter of lateral dominance and its relation to stuttering behavior, the activity of the subdominant hemisphere must be considered. As we have mentioned previously the subdominant hemisphere apparently takes over the tonal variations usually associated with all forms of musical experience. Children during this period are keenly interested in rhythmic activities and enjoy listening to stories and poems with rhyme. They also enjoy participating in choral speaking.

In considering the establishment of tonal sidedness it is especially interesting to observe that many children at 2½ and 3½ years of age quite customarily experience a period of excessive dysfluency which many call stuttering; however, these same children at four and five never again demonstrate any tendency toward stuttering. The ages at which the stuttering appears corresponds to the period during which the child is developing lateral dominance and during which, it might be conjectured, there is considerable neurological confusion in both perceiving and producing speech. By four, however, with sidedness well on the way to being established, the speech disturbance ceases.

It is of additional interest to consider that individuals with stuttering behavior at any age are always able to sing, perform unison choral speaking, and speak to rhythmic activities of various kinds with none of the customary hesitation and associated symptoms of stuttering normally characterizing their speech. During these periods of freedom from stuttering, it could be argued, various elements of tonality are being utilized to produce speech, and the subdominant hemisphere has become dominant in a neurological organization where hemisphere dominance has not occurred, where there may be too much balance between the two. Thus, there is no longer any struggle—at least temporarily. The writer recalls one young teenager with severe stuttering symptoms (also with confused laterality) who would go off alone where he would sing loudly and very fluently, if not proficiently, for long periods. He required these song sessions, he reported, to restore his strength and to relieve his feelings of frustration. The brain apparently can become just as weary as the body!

By the age of seven or eight in the normally well-organized child, dominance will have been established. As Delacato reminds us, hemisphere dominance is exclusive to man—and man is the only creature who can speak, read and write (Delacato, 1963).

Now having as a frame of reference a logical proposal for neurological developmental growth, we are ready to consider in more detail what is known or speculated about neural pathways involved in the speech process. We shall assume in the following discussion a normal neurological development, hemisphere dominance properly established, and a speech apparatus free of structural abnormalities.

Sensory Input—Audition

Although speech may be a response to any number of various stimuli—one, for example, may exclaim, "Ouch," in response to bumping one's head—we shall assume in this case that speech was in response to a question asked by another individual who expected a reply. We begin, therefore, with a brief consideration of the anatomy of the structure concerned with hearing—the ear.

The ear is divided into three parts: the external ear, middle ear and internal ear.

The External Ear. This is composed of the external acoustic meatus (auditory canal) and the pinna. The pinna, a cartilaginous framework covered with skin, projects from the side of the head and serves to collect and direct sound waves into the acoustic meatus. The external acoustic meatus, slightly over an inch in length, leads from the outside to the tympanic membrane (ear drum) separating the external ear from the middle ear. Along the upper wall of the meatus are cerumenous glands which secrete ear wax. This acts with the fine hair also present to prevent foreign particles and insects from entering the ear.

The Middle Ear. The middle ear is a tiny air cavity located in the temporal bone. The *Eustachian tubes* connect the cavity with the nasopharynx, equalizing air pressure within the cavity with that outside. There is an opening through the posterior wall into the mastoid antrum and mastoid cells.

Two tiny muscles are contained within the middle ear—*tensor tympani* and *stapedius.* The action of these muscles is not clear; however, since the action of most muscles is so frequently antagonistic, one muscle, it has been logically assumed, serves to force the footplate of stapes farther into the oval window while the other acts to withdraw it. Others believe both muscles act reflexively to protect the inner ear against excessively loud noises. Tympani is innervated by C-V, and stapedius by C-VII.

Two openings covered with membranes (the *round* and *oval*

windows) separate the middle ear from the inner ear. A chain of three small bones (*ossicles*) connect the tympanic membrane to the oval window. *Malleus* (hammer), *incus* (anvil) and *stapes* (stirrup) resemble their common names in appearance. (The miniature structure of the ossicles—the smallest bones in the body—should be noted. The opening of the stirrup, for example is the size of a pin head.)

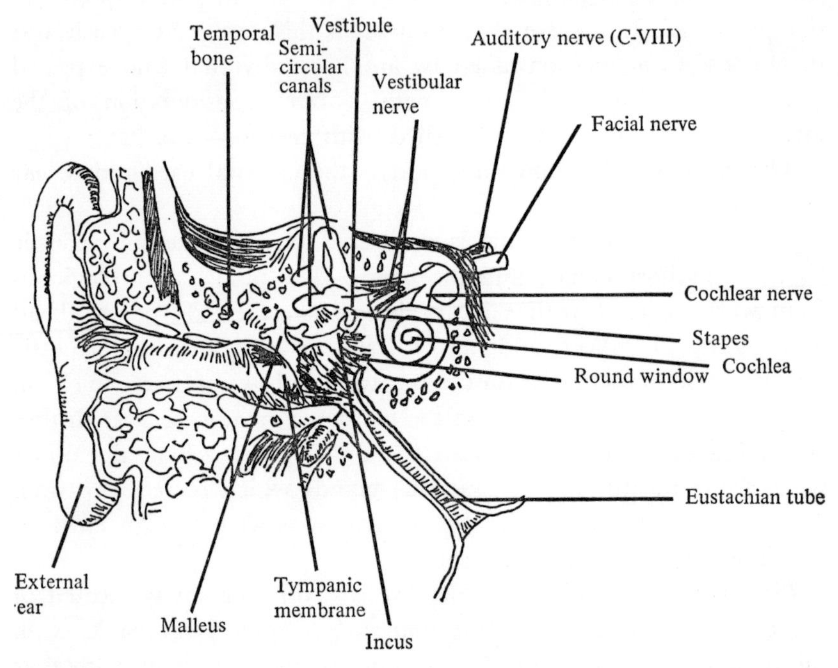

FIGURE 10-1. The auditory mechanism showing the outer, middle and inner ear.

The Inner Ear. This part of the ear is so complex that it has properly been called the labyrinth. There are three major divisions within the inner ear: the *vestibule, semicircular canals,* and the *cochlea.*

The *vestibule* is what its name suggests—an entranceway into various passages. Ovoid in shape, the vestibule contains the *saccule* and *utricle,* membranous sacs connected by Hensen's ducts. From the utricle three *semicircular canals* develop. (The semicircular canals, innervated by the vestibular branch of C-VIII, are organs of equilibrium. Although in certain instances where balance is impaired there is also a concommitant hearing loss, e.g., Meniere's disease, the canals will not be discussed further in this section.) The vestibule is a common meeting place for the fluid of the cochlea and of the semicircular canals through its five orifices.

The bony *cochlea* looks somewhat like a snail shell, thus its name. It contains a cochlear axis from its base to its apex called the *modiolus* around which it winds for two and three quarters turns. The cochlea might be thought of as three tubes (scalae) within one: the *scala tympani, scala vestibuli* and *scale media* (cochlear duct). Figure 10 shows the various divisions. The *basilar membrane,* it should be noted, projects from the peripheral border of the modiolus at a shelf-like projection called the *osseous spiral lamina* across to the peripheral border of the cochlea subdividing the larger tube into two separate scalae: vestibuli and tympani. At the apex (*helicotrema*) of the cochlea the two scalae are continuous. Both scalae contain a liquid called perilymph.

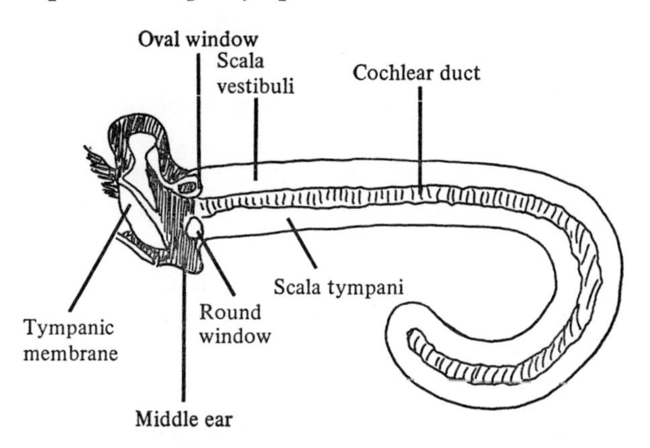

FIGURE 10-2. The cochlea as if it were uncurled.

The scala media (cochlear duct) is a subdivision of scala tympani. It is separated from tympani by a delicate membrane, *Reissner's membrane,* extending diagonally at about a forty-five degree angle with the basilar membrane which forms its floor. Scala media ends in a cul-de-sac near the helicotrema. It contains a liquid called endolymph. The *organ of Corti* is located in the scala media.

On the floor of the scala media, resting on the basilar membrane and extending gently into the *reticular membrane* above, are the inner rods of Corti. (There are approximately 6,000 outer rods and 4,000 inner rods.) Overhanging the entire organ of Corti is another membrane, the *tectorial membrane.* Also lying on the floor of media are specialized cells known as the inner and outer hair cells. From each cell 12 to 20 cilia—minute hairs—project into the endolymph. Although estimates vary, there are approximately 25,000 inner and outer hair cells.

It is in the organ of Corti that contact is made with the nerve endings of the acoustic branch of C-VIII. Exactly what occurs to fire the nerve impulse resulting in the eventual auditory impulses perceived in the brain is not clear. Whether the primary factor is physical, chemical, electrical, or a combination of two or all of these, is a subject of considerable interest to speech scientists and audiologists, and discussed at considerable detail in relation to auditory perception. Also of additional interest are the various theories of hearing which attempt to clarify exactly what happens in the organ of Corti as sound is perceived there and transmitted to higher centers. We shall mention here only one such theory since it seems more appropriate to consider all the various theories in relation to courses in psycho-acoustics or audiology.

In 1875 Hermann von Helmoltz postulated what was known as the *resonance* or *harp* theory. The theory assumed that the 24,000, more or less, fibers making up the basilar membrane are tuned to different frequencies as are the strings of a piano or harp. Thus, when sound waves containing those frequencies are received by the ear, the appropriate fibers resonate automatically stimulating the hair cells of the organ of Corti resting on those fibers of the membrane. The stimulation consequently produces impulses in the auditory branch of C-VIII. Since the transverse fibers at the base of the cochlea are short, they resonate to high pitches; the lower fibers near the apex resonate to lower pitches.

Auditory Stages

Although there is considerable disagreement regarding the specific aspects of various levels of activity as the initial auditory impulse is received and processed to the cortex where it is finally interpreted, it is possible to present in logical order the various staging areas involved in audition.

At what might be called *stage one,* the sound waves strike the tympanic membrane causing it to vibrate. Since malleus is attached to the membrane, it, in turn, vibrates thus causing the other ossicles to vibrate. Since stapes in turn thrusts itself into the oval window the vibrations are passed on to the fluid in the inner ear. The various sound impulses are now transmitted via the medium of the movable liquid. The frequency of each impulse determines, apparently, the route to the organ of Corti in the scala media. Some impulses, it is thought, are transmitted through the scale vestibuli, helicotrema, scale tympani and finally to the organ of Corti in the scale media; others stimulate the organ of Corti directly without taking the long route. The pressure principle is responsible for this activity in the incompressible fluid of the inner ear. It should be noted that the round window bulges into the middle ear as the various impulses are received, thus providing for the expansion necessitated by the pulsations of the liquid.

At *stage two,* the pulsations are programmed or coded in a way that may be comparable to feeding information into an IBM machine for computation. What happens at this stage is, as we have mentioned, obscure. However, by some means, physical, chemical, electrical, or some other, the nerve impulses are fired off in the organ of Corti and their transmission to the cortex initiated.

At *stage three,* apparently, some beginning synthesis occurs. At this stage perhaps we may become completely confounded by the bewildering array of events which evidently must occur. One needs only to pause momentarily and listen to whatever sound environment is available. The awareness of the various dimensions of sound is at once evident. One perceives frequency (pitch), loudness, quality, rate, intonation of spoken speech; in addition, sound discrimination, sound localization, and sound selectivity are all present depending on our focus of attention. To conclude that all these activities are initiated by a tiny transmitter in the inner ear is scarcely logical; yet such seems to be the case—at least in a very fundamental sense.

At *stage four,* the final stage of synthesis occurs. In stage three only the physical aspects of sound were experienced; now, and perhaps even more profoundly, the various sounds are interpreted, associated, and finally understood. With fantastic IBM precision the information has been received by us.

The Neuroanatomy of Audition

There appear to be a succession of four neurons from the cochlea to the temporal lobe involved in transmitting the auditory impulses. The bipolar *first-order* cells forming neurons in the modiolus—25,000 to 29,000 originating on the internal or external hair cells—form the spiral ganglion of the cochlea. As the acoustic branch of C-VIII, the fibers leave the temporal bone through the internal meatus. As masses of gray matter in the ventral and dorsal cochlear neuclei in the upper medulla and pons, they synapse with secondary neurons.

About half of the *second-order* neurons in the cochlear nuclei cross in the pons where some synapse in the superior olivary complex (as do some of the uncrossed fibers) and then ascend in a myelinated tract on each side, the lateral lemniscus, through the pons to the midbrain. In the midbrain, after synapsing with *third-order* neurons in the inferior colliculi, they continue to another station in the thalamus, the medial geniculate body.

The final, or *fourth-order,* neurons reach the superior temporal gyrus designated by Brodmann as area 41. Here, it is thought, is the primary receptive area for hearing.

Since approximately 50 per cent of the nerve fibers do not cross, impulses from both ears reach their corresponding temporal lobes. The removal of one temporal lobe does not consequently cause deafness in either ear. However, especially in adults, the removal of the dominant temporal lobe impairs associations and decreases the ability to understand speech.

Since the number of nerve impulses from the ear to the cortex progressively decreases, the temporal lobe, it could be argued, is not concerned with all the auditory processes mentioned previously in stages three and four. The circumstances, apparently, support what Penfield (1959) believes about functional subdivisions of the cortex.

> Each functional subdivision of the cerebral cortex of man may be looked upon as an outgrowth or projection outward of some area of gray matter in the lower brain stem. Thus the projected area in the

newly formed cortex presumably serves to amplify and enlarge a function already being served in a rudimentary manner by the old brain of more elementary animals.

Thus, in connection with audition, Penfield would probably consider the temporal lobe as a type of arrival platform subservient to a central integrating system situated within the higher brain stem—in this case, the pons and mesencephalon. If we accept Penfield's proposal, considering the diminishing number of nerve fibers along the auditory route, it seems logical to conclude that a great deal of the processing of auditory stimuli—pitch, loudness, etc.—occurs *before* the impulse reaches the temporal lobe. Perhaps since man alone is able to speak, and since he alone has lateral dominance, the temporal lobe is the primary source of the word formulation processes—not, however, of word meanings since dogs and other animals do seem to understand the meaning of certain words. To some extent, then, even word comprehension may be the product of the central integrating system described by Penfield—not the cortex alone.

The Speech Process

It is now assumed that recognition of the auditory input has occurred and the individual is ready to reply. What happens when the words are finally selected, spoken, and presumably perceived once again by the individual who initiated the conversation in the first place?

Penfield's clinical observations suggest that comprehension of speech occurs after impulses have been received in the higher brain stem (central integrating system) and both cortical auditory areas; and during interaction between the higher brain stem and the left hemisphere. Following interaction between the higher brain stem and the left hemisphere, impulses are transmitted to both cortical motor areas and then to the final common motor pathways—the corticospinal tracts—to those muscles necessary to produce speech.

Penfield does not consider any one area of the brain to be all important in the speech process. Instead, he believes several cortical areas acting along with a central integrating system at the high brain stem level are involved. The most important area for speech, he believes, is the posterior temporoparietal region, including the posterior parts of the first, second, and third temporal convolutions, the supramarginal gyrus and the angular gyrus. Figure 3 shows many of these areas.

The next most significant area for speech, according to Penfield, is Broca's area including the three gyri anterior to the precentral face area. The supplementary motor area on the medial and slightly on the superior part of the hemisphere in front of the precentral foot area is, he believes, important, but dispensable. Lesions in this area, apparently, may produce prolonged aphasia. If other areas for speech are destroyed, this area, if still intact, then becomes of much greater importance. Apparently, if one speech area is destroyed, adjacent areas of the cortex will continue to function during speech.

Kaplan (1960) has presented what he considers to be the neurological speech processes in somewhat more detail than Penfield. He recognizes hemisphere dominance to be a controversial area; apparently, however, he considers the establishment of dominance to be important. At birth the hemispheres seem to have equal potentialities; the angular gyrus (Brodmann 39)—a type of switchboard for routing and integrating diverse impulses—appears to be bilaterally functional. However, for reasons as yet unknown, one hemisphere takes control. Kaplan suggests that it may be difficult or impossible to synthesize meaningful concepts about the same stimulus simultaneously in both hemispheres. It should be remembered, however, that Delacato insists that a period of bilateral activity is essential to normal neurological development, and cautions against forcing the child into one-sidedness too early.

It is interesting to consider why right-handedness has become so common in our own as well as other cultures where handedness is not necessarily encouraged by the environment. If, as Penfield believes, the left hemisphere is important for speech, to what extent is this related to right dominance? Does right dominance develop because of the presence of important speech areas in the left hemisphere? Man alone has developed lateral dominance; he alone has developed speech. Is there a relationship?

Clinical evidence indicates the major significance of the angular gyrus in the total speech process. Surgical removal of the non-dominant angular gyrus causes no appreciable decrease in intelligence but removal of the dominant angular gyrus reduces intelligence to that of an idiot. However, when the dominant gyrus is excised in a young child, the opposite side takes over with little or no effect.

Kaplan describes an *ideamotor center* in the supramarginal gyrus of the dominant parietal lobe. When this area receives impulses, it consciously and automatically decides a course of action by reflexively selecting words and sentences used in conversation. The ideamotor center, however, is inhibited by the prefrontal cortex so the reflex activity of the center is subjected to a kind of censorship. (In some ways this proposal is comparable to Freud's concept of the super ego or conscience.) In any event, the monitoring and selection of ideas now appears to be a definite function of the prefrontal cortex. The idea-motor center having finally received feedback from the prefrontal area now transmits the impulses to Broca's area. From here impulses are transmitted to motor areas in the cortex (Brodmann 4, 6) where the various organs of speech are set into motion via efferent nerve tracts leading to the end organs.

The route down involves every neurological level. From areas 4 and 6 the speech impulse passes on to the basal ganglia, to the thalamus and hypothalamus, to the pons and medulla and finally to the cord. Along the route a bewildering number of synapses are being made, with various cranial nerves originating in the pons and medulla activating muscles of articulation, phonation and resonation. Muscle tone as well as muscle inhibition are all being temporarily regulated by various motor impulses being sent over numerous tracts. Spinal peripheral nerves are fired to activate the muscles of respiration; autonomic fibers are beginning to impose subtle influences on surface textures and bodily rhythms. A gigantic, profoundly involved apparatus is operating. In awe, we can only make feeble conjectures about its functioning.

Chapter 6

RESPIRATION

IN ORDER TO initiate sound for speech, some force is necessary. The airstream provides the necessary source for phonation as well as for articulation as we shall see.

THE RESPIRATORY SYSTEM

All organisms exchange gases with their environment. Even the single-celled amoeba obtains oxygen as well as nutrients, and discharges carbon dioxide through the cell membrane. To obtain oxygen and discharge waste, higher organisms require a special apparatus—the respiratory apparatus.

External Respiration

The human body takes in oxygen and discharges carbon dioxide by breathing, or external respiration. The process consists of taking air into the lungs (inspiration) and expelling air from the lungs (expiration). The inspired air passes through the nasal chambers, pharynx, larynx, trachea, right and left bronchi, and finally, the air sacs (alveoli) of the lungs. By diffusion, the red blood cells, coursing through the lungs, take in oxygen from the air and discharge carbon dioxide into it. The expired carbon dioxide returns via the same passageways to the outside. The pharynx, it should be noted, is a foodway as well as an airway.

Air, it should be observed, is not drawn into the lungs by the mere force of inspiration alone; instead, the diaphragm—a great dome-shaped muscle separating the thorax from the abdominal cavity—and additional muscles in the abdominal and thoracic regions contract, increasing the size of the thorax containing the lungs. In addition, the elevation of the sternum, rib cage and shoulder girdle provides space in the upper chest cavity. Since air flows to areas where pressure is below atmospheric level, the increased space provided by the action just described results in an influx of air into the lungs which now have greater room for expansion.

In expiration, the process is reversed. *Muscle relaxation, gravity,* and *inertia* all function to restore the thoracic cavity to its previous dimensions. Thus, the air is forced out to begin the cycle anew. As we shall see, although the process is essentially similar, for speech purposes more work needs to be done to provide for the additional air needed for producing adequate oral speech.

Internal Respiration

Within the body cells, in contrast to the interaction of blood and air in the lungs, a reverse process occurs. Here the circulating blood gives off oxygen to the tissues and takes carbon dioxide from them. The oxygen in the tissue cells combines with other substances repeatedly broken down into simpler oxygen-absorbing elements until only carbon dioxide and water remain in the tissues. The chemical change (oxidation) releases energy to the tissues for use in bodily activities. The exchange of gases between the blood and the body cells is called internal respiration. Some tissues, like muscles and glands, use up considerable energy, especially in strenuous activity, and consequently discharge more carbon dioxide and require large quantities of oxygen. Oxygen cannot be stored in the body, but must be constantly replenished through the circulation of the blood.

Hyperventilation. Occasionally, the balance between carbon dioxide and oxygen in the circulating blood becomes disturbed—during deep-breathing exercises, for example. Too much oxyen accumulates, and one may experience the sensation of dizziness or light-headedness; on the other hand, excessive carbon dioxide accumulation may cause fatigue and apathy (*hypoventilation*).

Although the nose, mouth, pharynx, and larynx are vital passageways for the transmission of air into the lungs (during speech breathing) their anatomy will not be included in this unit. Each will be discussed in subsequent chapters in relation to other aspects of oral speech production.

Trachea

Assuming the air has been taken in through the nose, has been passed down along the pharyngeal divisions (nasopharynx, oropharynx, laryngopharynx) through the larynx with vocal folds abducted, it now reaches the *trachea* attaching directly to the most inferior cartilage (cricoid) of the larynx.

The trachea is cartilagenous anteriorly but has smooth fibers posteriorly which give inward to provide space for a bolus of food passing down the esophagus directly posterior to it. The *trachealis* muscle, in the dorsal portion of the trachea, innervated by C-X and the sympathetic division of ANS, relaxes during inspiration thus enlarging the lumen of the trachea. During expiration, especially during forced expiration, the muscle contracts and the lumen of the tube decreases in size. The mucous membrane lining of the trachea is continuous above and below with the larynx and bronchi, respectively.

Bronchi

At the inferior margins of the trachea at about the level of the fifth thoracic vertebra, the trachea divides into the right (shorter) and left primary bronchi. The structure of the primary bronchi is the same as the trachea except the cartilaginous rings are complete. On entering the lungs, the primary bronchi divide into a number of branches, secondary bronchi, which in turn divide into smaller and smaller divisions called bronchioles. Each bronchiole continues to one or more respiratory bronchioles which, in turn, give off several branches called alveolar ducts into which the alveoli open directly, or through an intervening structure, the alveolar sac.

Lungs

The lungs are cone-shaped organs lying in the pleural cavities of the thorax. The base of each lung contacts the upper surface of the diaphragm, extending to the level of the seventh rib anteriorly and the eleventh rib posteriorly (see Fig. 11). The space between the two lungs, called the *mediastinum,* contains the heart, great vessels, the thymus gland, the esophagus, some nerves, a portion of the trachea, and the primary bronchi.

Each lung is covered by a delicate membrane, the *pleura.* The

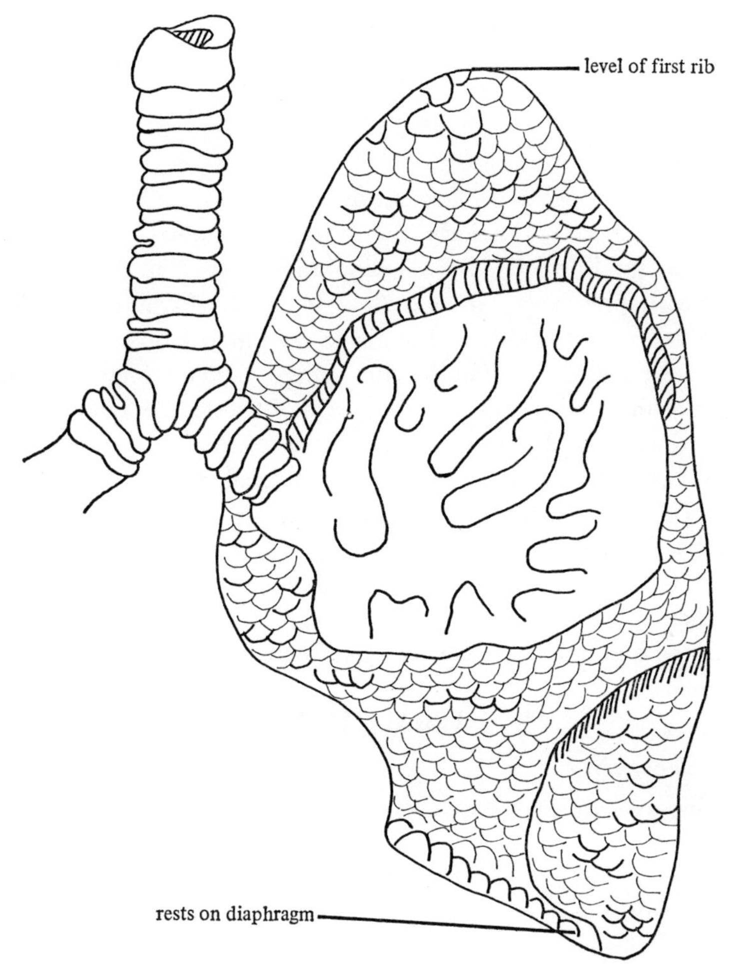

FIGURE 11. The tracheobronchial tree and the left lung.

two layers of pleura are separated by a thin layer of fluid. Normally the layers are so closely in apposition, that the space between them is potential rather than real.

Because of the extreme elasticity of the lung tissue, the lungs always fill the pleural area of the thoracic cavity no matter what its volume. It is this principle which establishes the respiratory cycle.

Thoracic Cavity

The lungs are contained within the thoracic cavity. Anteriorly and medially the thoracic cavity is bounded by the sternum (composed of the *manubrium, corpus,* and *xiphoid process*) and the costal cartilages which attach the seven upper ribs directly to the sternum. Of the twelve ribs on each side, ribs eight, nine, and ten also attach to the sternum but indirectly via long cartilages; ribs eleven and twelve are free floating. Posteriorly, all twelve ribs attach to the thoracic vertebrae. Superiorly, the thorax is bounded by the clavicles and scapulae; inferiorly, by the diaphragm (see Fig. 12).

As stated previously, air will flow to areas where pressure is below atmospheric level; thus for air to be inhaled, it is necessary to increase the space containing the lungs thereby increasing their volume as the air is taken in. To provide for this, the anteroposterior diameter and the transverse diameter of the thoracic cage are increased by elevation of the ribs. The vertical diameter is increased chiefly by the descent of the diaphragm.

Real work is done to provide for the space adjustments necessary during respiration. And, as one might expect, the more air needed for either strenuous physical activities or for producing speech, the greater the amount of work necessary.

INHALATION

Rest Breathing

During rest breathing, for life purposes only, the work done to enlarge the thoracic cavity during inhalation is so habitual and involuntary, we are rarely aware of the process. The following muscles are, however, actively working, assuming, of course, a normal structure.

Diaphragm. The diaphragm is a muscleotendinuous portion completely separating the thoracic and abdominal cavities. Dome-shaped, all its fibers insert superiorly into a common aponeurotic *central tendon.* Posteriorly, it is attached to the first few lumbar vertebrae; anteriorly, at the xiphoid process and costal cartilages of the lower six ribs. Contraction draws the central tendon down and slightly forward, pushing the stomach and viscera out, resulting in an increase in the vertical diameter of the thorax. The maximum excursion of which the diaphragm is capable is somewhat less than three inches. For normal life purposes, the excursion is usually

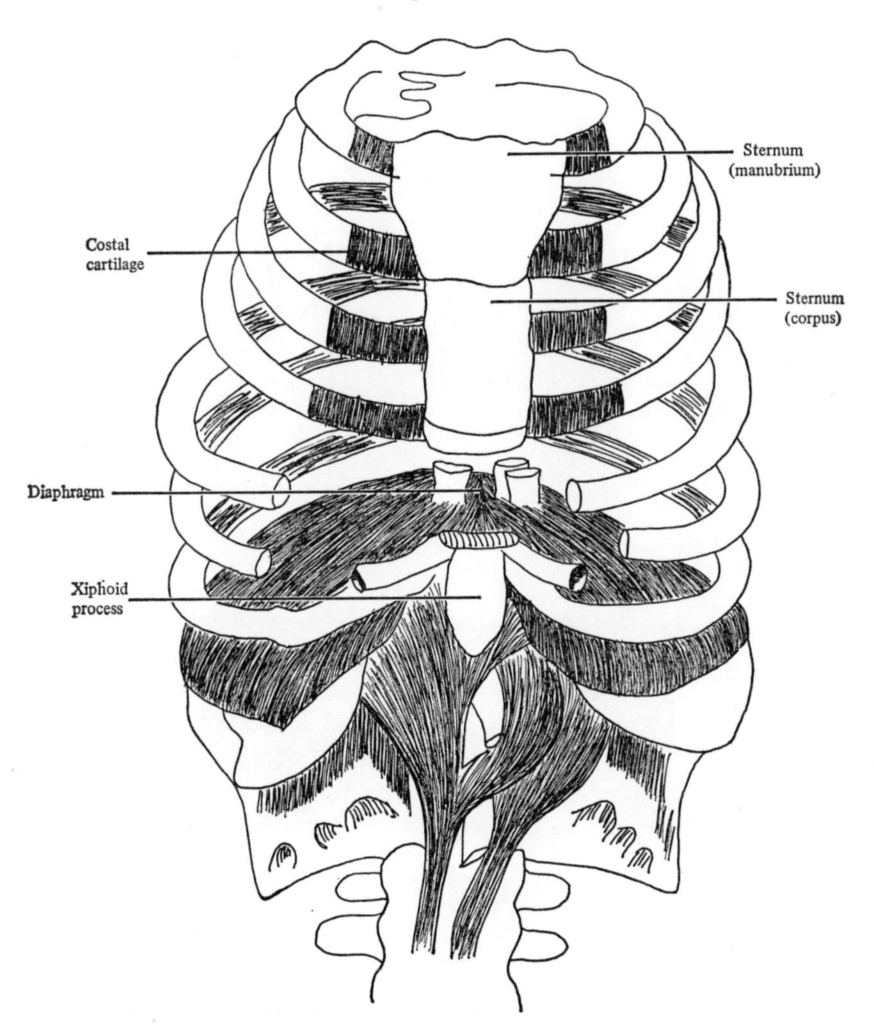

FIGURE 12. The thorax showing the sternum, ribs, costal cartilages and diaphragm.

slightly less than one inch. The diaphragm is innervated by the *phrenic* nerve (see Fig. 12).

External Intercostals. The external intercostals extend from the vertebral column posteriorly to the lateral margins of the costal cartilages anteriorly, attaching from the inferior margin of each rib to the superior margin of the rib beneath. The eleven pairs are

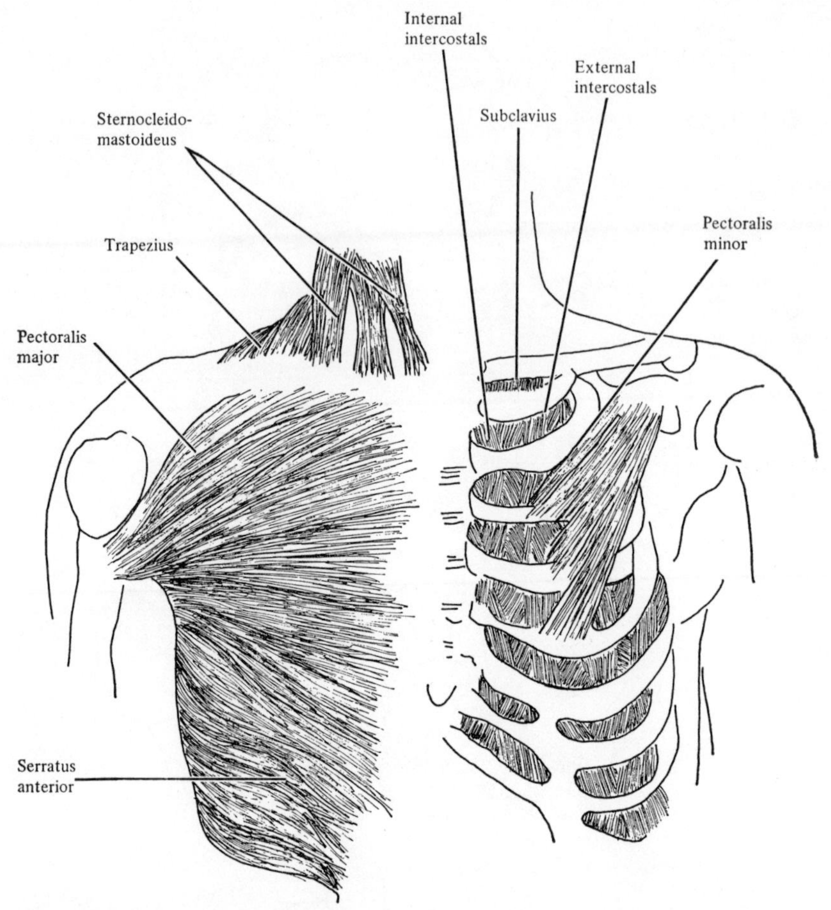

FIGURE 13. Anterior portion of thorax showing some muscles of inhalation.

innervated by T1-11. (Thoracic nerves do not form plexuses but pass out in intercostal spaces as the intercostal nerves.) Their action is to elevate the rib cage upward and slightly laterally (see Figs. 13 and 15).

Internal Intercostals. The internal intercostals are deep to the externals, run obliquely like the externals, but at a different (right) angle. Originating at the sternum, the eleven pairs do not extend posteriorly farther than the angles of the ribs. Innervated by T1-11, their action is to aid in the elevation of the ribs (see Figs. 13 and 15).

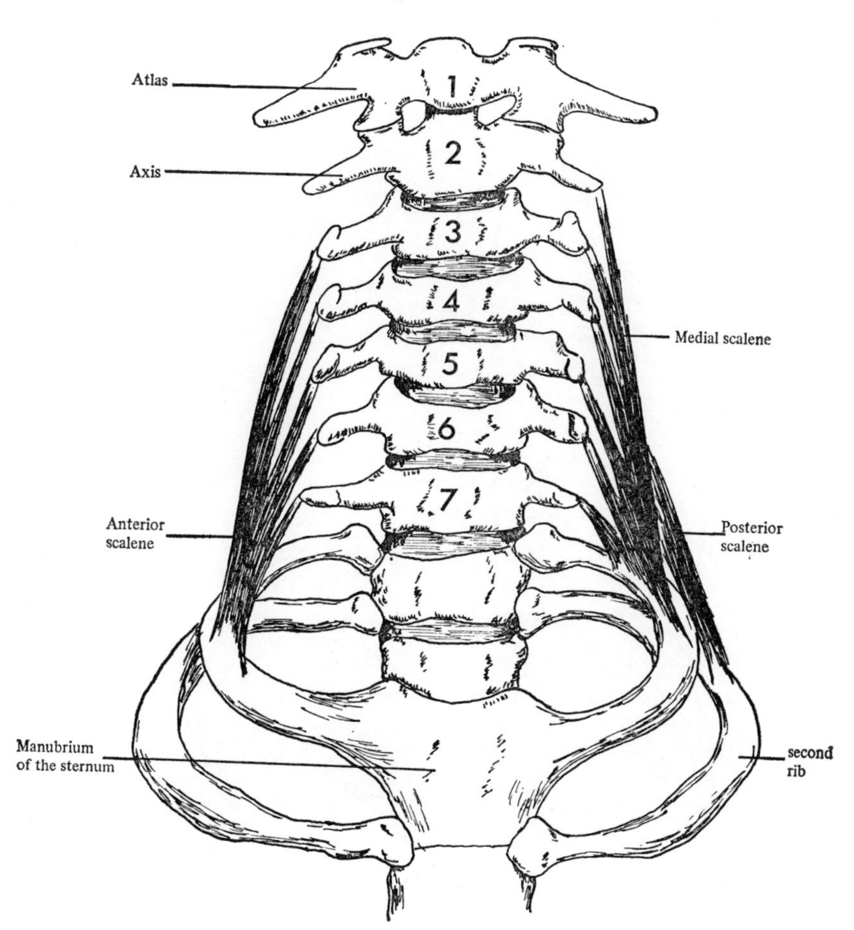

FIGURE 14. The scalene muscles.

Scalene. Anterior, medial, and posterior pairs all attach from cervical vertebrae 3-7 to either rib one (anterior and medial) or rib two (posterior). Anterior innervated by C5-7; medial by C4-8; and posterior by C-7 and C-8, all act to fix the upper two ribs. During forced inhalation, especially if clavicular breathing is used, these muscles also assist in elevating the upper ribs (see Figs. 14 and 16).

Levatores Costarum. The twelve pairs of levatores attach from the transverse process of the seventh cervicle and eleven upper thoracic vertebrae to the next rib below; ending between the angle

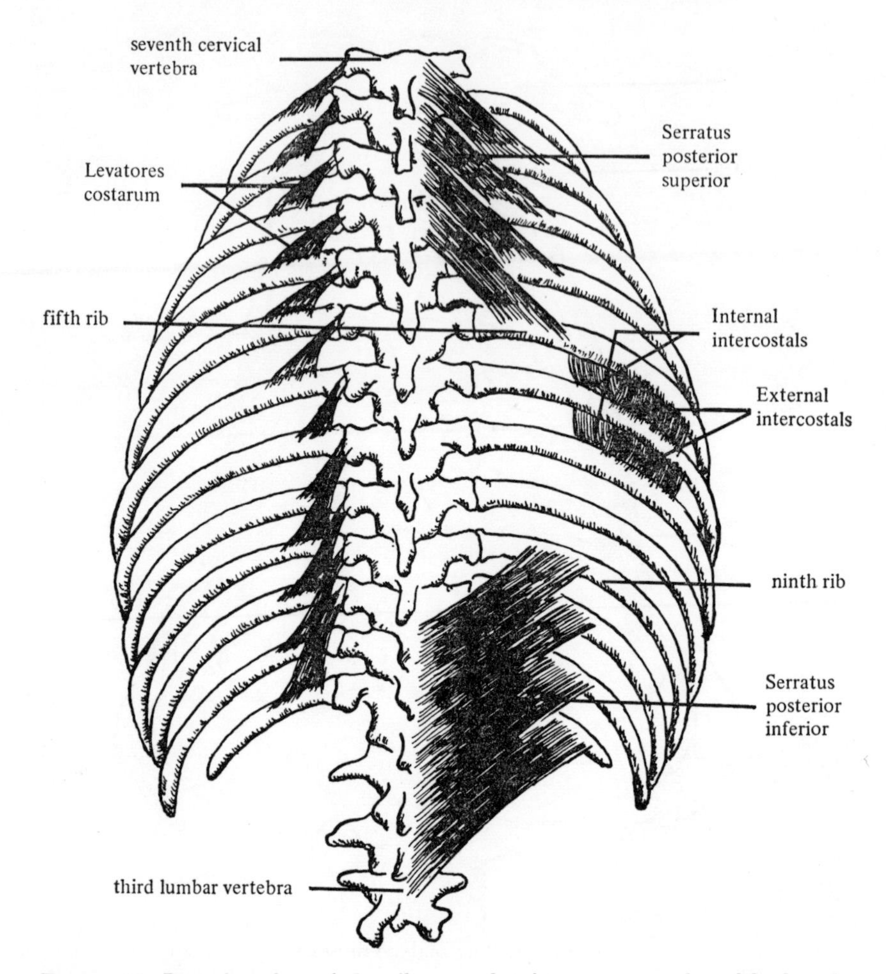

FIGURE 15. Posterior view of the rib cage showing some muscles of both quiet and forced inhalation.

and tubercle of each rib, the four last in this group attach to the two ribs below. Innervated by C-8 and T1-11, they elevate the ribs and help to rotate and extend the vertebral column (see Fig. 15).

Sacrospinalis. This paired, cord-like muscle lies in the groove on the side of the vertebral column posteriorly. It arises from the posterior part of the iliac crest, the posterior surface of the sacrum, and from the spinous process of all lumbar vertebrae and the last two thoracic vertebrae. The muscle separates in the upper lumbar region into three columns: lateral or iliocostalis, middle or longissimus dorsi, and medial or spinalis dorsi. Iliocostalis inserts into the angles of the lower five or six ribs. Longissimus, the largest and most powerful, has a double set of insertions on the transverse processes of the thoracic vertebrae and the backs of the ribs which give it firm grip for extension. Spinalis dorsi inserts into the spines of the thoracic vertebrae. Innervated by the various spinal nerves at corresponding levels, this muscle, because it is the deepest layer among back muscles and because of its various divisions, has variable function. Primarily as an extensor maintaining the spine erect against gravity, it does assist in the elevation of the rib cage; however, some of its divisions may also act to depress the rib cage during expiration.

Forced Inhalation

Sometimes during strenuous exercise or during oral speech production more breath is required. To enable more air to enter the thoracic cavity, the same principle of atmospheric pressure mentioned previously must be considered. The thoracic cavity must be additionally enlarged to permit the lungs to expand further than for rest breathing purposes. To accomplish this, more work needs to be done; all of the muscles utilized rest for breathing act more forcefully; some or all of the following new muscles (depending on the requirement) are used.

Serratus Posterior Superior. This paired muscle attaches variably from the spinous processes of the last cervical and first two thoracic vertebrae to the upper borders of the second to fifth ribs. Innervated by T1-4, its action is to raise the ribs and thus enlarge the thorax (see Fig. 15).

Serratus Posterior Inferior. This paired muscle attaches from the spinous processes of the last two thoracic and first two lumbar vertebrae to the lower border of the last four ribs. Innervated by T-9, T-10, and T-11, its action is thought by some to assist the diaphragm in forced inspiration by fixating the lower ribs or, by pulling the lower ribs outward, enlarging the lateral dimension of the thorax. On the other hand, it may also assist in expiration by pulling the lower ribs down and decreasing the volume of the thorax. Until more conclusive evidence is obtained, it seems logical to think of this muscle as primarily a muscle of forced inhalation (see Fig. 15).

Serratus Anterior. This paired muscle attaches from the inferior angle of the scapula to the eight or nine upper ribs. Innervated by C-5, C-6, and C-7. When the shoulders are fixed, it assists in elevating the ribs (see Fig. 13).

Pectoralis Major. A paired muscle, pectoralis major attaches from the bicipital ridge of the humerus to the sternum, clavicle, and the second to seventh costal cartilages. Innervated by C-6, C-7, C-8, and T-1, its action is to elevate the ribs when the shoulders are fixed (see Fig. 13).

Pectoralis Minor. Paired, pectoralis minor attaches from the carocoid process of the scapula to ribs two through five. Innervated by C-7 and C-8, its action is to elevate the ribs when the scapula is fixed (see Fig. 13).

Latissimus Dorsi. Paired, latissimus attaches from the bicipital groove of the humerus to the lower six thoracic vertebrae and to the lumbar and sacral vertebrae, the four lowest ribs, and the crest of the ilium. Innervated by C-6, C-7, and C-8, its action is primarily to rotate the humerus internally and is not considered important to respiration by some; however, during contraction, it appears logical to believe this muscle assists in the elevation of the lower ribs if the arms are fixed (see Fig. 16).

Subclavius. Paired, subclavius attaches from the lower surface of the clavicle to the first rib. Innervated by C-5 and C-6, its action elevates the upper thorax, especially in cases of clavicular breathing (see Fig. 13).

Sternocleidomastoideus. Paired, this muscle, as its name suggests, arises from two heads, one from the sternum and one from the clavicle, and inserts into the mastoid process and the superior oblique line of the occipital bone. Innervated by C-XI, its action elevates the upper thorax when the head is fixed, especially during clavicular breathing (see Fig. 13).

In addition to the muscles mentioned, those acting upon the shoulder girdle to fix it are sometimes included among the muscles of forced inhalation. *Trapezius, rhomboideus major, rhomboideus minor, levator scapulae,* and *deltoideus* all attach to the scapula and by their action fixate the shoulder.

All of the extrinsic muscles of the larynx (discussed in Chap. 7)

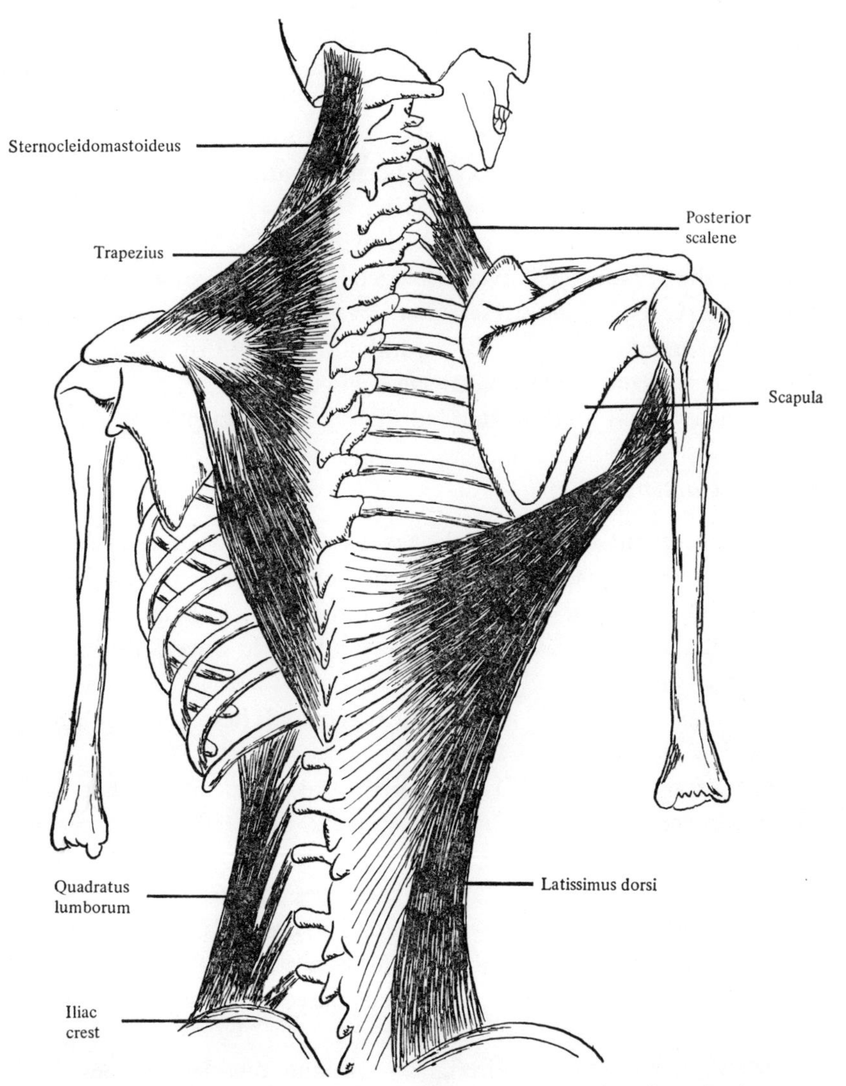

FIGURE 16. Posterior view of the thorax showing muscles of respiration.

are also thought to be involved in inhalation and exhalation in varying degrees. Their action, however, is comparatively insignificant.

EXHALATION

Passive Factors

In exhalation, the volume of the thoracic cavity containing the lungs is decreased and the air is expelled. Additional work is done to accomplish this; however, several factors operate requiring no work since their action is primarily the result of gravity and inertia. Called passive factors, therefore, they are as follows:

1. The heavy rib cage, having been elevated, will drop back to its natural position because of gravity.
2. The ribs, having been stretched, will recoil.
3. As the thoracic cavity is elevated the costal cartilages are rotated and placed under stress called torque. With relaxation of the muscles of inhalation, there is natural untorqueing of the cartilages.
4. Elastic recoil of the lung tissue occurs.
5. Elastic recoil of the extended viscera will occur.

Active Factors

A group of muscles located in the lower thoracic and abdominal areas assist in depressing the ribs and compressing the abdominal viscera. They are, therefore, called muscles of exhalation. These muscles can do little work during expiration, however, if the individual does not habitually breathe with considerable diaphragmatic excursion extending the abdominal viscera. These muscles are as follows.

Transverse Thoracis. This paired, sheet-like muscle has three parts: *sternocostalis, innermost intercostals* and *subcostals.* Sternocostalis arises from the back of the xyphoid process and corpus of the sternum and inserts into costal cartilages two to six. The innermost intercostals are deep to the internal intercostals. The subcostals lie on the internal surface of the lower ribs near their angles and pass over one or two spaces. Thoracic nerves innervate the various parts. The action depresses the rib cage.

Rectus Abdominus. Paired, this midline muscle attaches from the crest and symphysis of the pubis to the xiphoid process and costal cartilages of ribs five to seven. Innervated by T7-11, its action is to compress the abdominal viscera and depress the thorax (see Fig. 17).

External Oblique. Paired, this flat, broad muscle covers the surface of the lower thoracic and abdominal walls. Attaches from the crest of the ilium, crest of the pubis, linea alba via the abdominal aponeurosis to the lower eight ribs. Innervated by T5-12 and L-1,

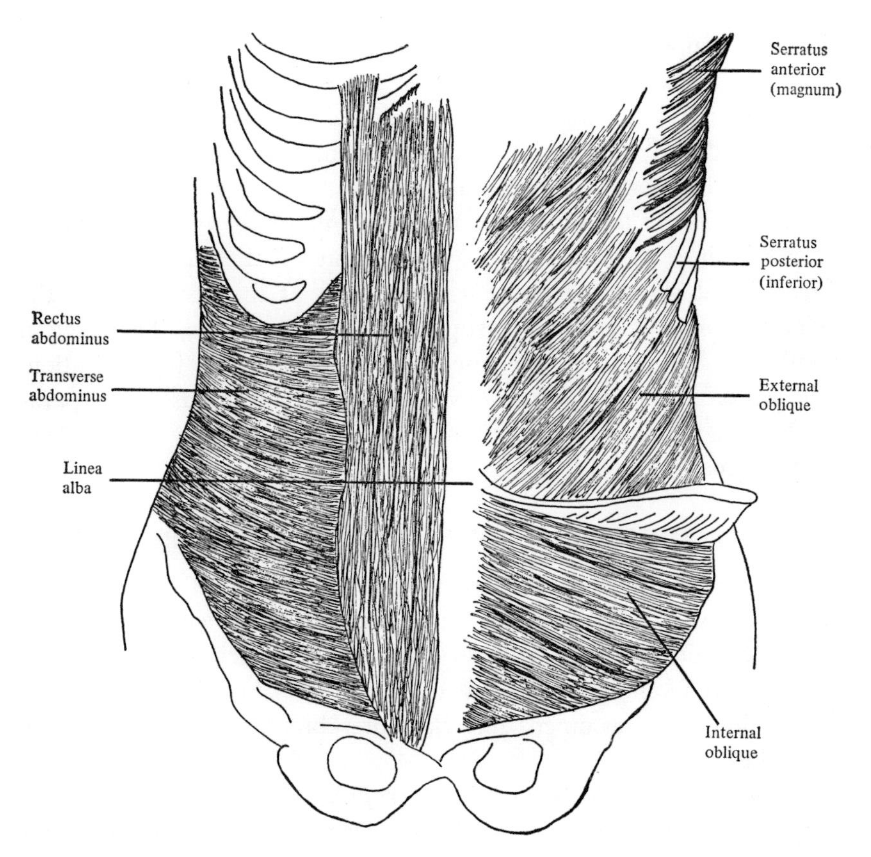

FIGURE 17. Anterior portion of thorax and abdomen showing muscles of inhalation and exhalation.

its action is to compress the abdominal viscera and depress the thorax (see Fig. 17).

Internal Oblique. Paired and deep to external oblique this muscle attaches from the crest of the ilium and lumbar fascia to the lower three or four ribs, crest of the iliac around the abdomen to insert via the abdominal aponeurosis into the linea alba. Innervated by T9-12 and L-1 its action is to depress the thorax (see Fig. 17).

Transversus Abdominus. Paired, this is the deepest of the anterior abdominal muscles. It attaches from the inner surfaces of the lowest six ribs, the lumbodorsal fascia, iliac crest, and inguinal ligament (superior spine of ilium to pubic tubercle) to the deepest layer of the abdominal aponeurosis and the linea alba; some few fibers extend to the pubis and the inguinal ligament. Innervated by T7-12 and L-1, the action compresses the abdominal viscera and depresses the thorax (see Fig. 17).

In addition to the muscles mentioned, *quadratus lumborum* (from crest of ilium to rib 12) fixes the origin of the diaphragm (see Fig. 16). *Levator ani* and *coccygeus* both at the very base of the spine are thought to unite to support the pelvic viscera. Their action would assist in pushing the viscera up, thus assisting in inspiration. The action of the subcostals, levator ani and coccygeus is comparatively very minor and would probably be utilized only during deep diaphragmatic breathing.

SPEECH BREATHING COMPARED TO REST BREATHING

Because breathing during oral speech production is so automatic, few are aware of the fundamental differences between inhalation and exhalation for life purposes and for producing speech. The following differences are present during normal breathing for speech production (it is assumed that clavicular breathing is not excessive or exclusive):

1. *Inhalation is deeper and more rapid.* The increases in inhalation is a natural consequence of the way we speak—in phrases and short sentences without interruption. To provide sufficient air to sustain what is generally considered normal phrasing, more air needs to be inhaled so that it may be expended over a longer period of time. The excursion of the diaphragm is normally approximately less than one inch during rest breathing. For speech, the excursion is approximately three inches.

In order to keep speech moving along without markedly noticeable interruptions, it is necessary not only to inhale more air, but also to accomplish it very rapidly. To accommodate for this, during speech, inhalation is done through the mouth rather than the nose.

2. *Rate and rhythm vary.* As a direct consequence of what has just been mentioned, there are sharp differences in the rate and rhythm of inhalation-exhalation time. During rest breathing, inspiration time is normally approximately 1¾ seconds and expiration 1¾

seconds. The total IE is 3½ seconds with a ratio of 1:1. During speech breathing, inspiration time is ¼ to ½ seconds and expiration three to four seconds. The total IE time is 3¼ seconds to 4½ seconds with a ratio of approximately 1:8.

During normal rest breathing, the total number of IE cycles is approximately fourteen to seventeen per minute. (This number is, of course, subject to considerable change depending on physical activity, temperature changes, emotional attitudes, and blood variations.) During speech breathing, the total number of IE cycles is considerably less because of the reasons just mentioned. In some cases where speech breathing is extremely poor, the IE ratio may become so improperly balanced that the speaker will suffer from either hyper- or hypoventilation.

3. *Exhalation is more forceful and controlled.* Since the expended air is put under pressure by the elastic nature of the lung tissue and by the contraction of the various muscles, its expenditure is consequently more forceful when it is permitted to escape. The air is expended gradually in what some call a syllable pulse.

Certain phonemes require a greater air expenditure than others. Fricatives, for example, require a greater total air expenditure than plosives. Vowels require even less air expenditure; voiced, less than for voiceless sounds. As pitch increases, vocal cord adduction increases and less and less air is expended. As the soprano vocalizes an extremely high note to conclude her performance she appears suspended, permitting only the barest trickle of air to escape over the finely adjusted vocal cords.

4. *Cerebral cortex controls speech breathing.* Rest breathing is unconscious and involuntary. The respiratory center is situated in a groove in the medulla called *calamus scriptorius.* This center is influenced by stimuli arising in the lungs in the alveoli containing stretch receptors. When the alveoli are inflated afferent proprioceptive impulses travel to the medulla via C-X to inhibit the center and terminate the inspiration. At a given point, a second set of impulses are transmitted from other alveolar stretch receptors which stimulate the center to initiate the next inspiration. The entire process, known as the Hering-Breuer reflex, is self-regulating, receiving guidelines from the pH of the blood.

In speech breathing, as stated previously, there is control of both inspiration and expiration. To provide for this, volition is needed, necessitating the use of the cerebrum. For many, the act of speech breathing has been learned so well and become so automatic it might very well be considered functionally autonomous; however, for others, the process, probably because it was poorly learned, or for varying other psychic reasons preventing normal usage, is a very conscious affair frequently causing much distress.

Types of Speech Breathing

For reasons which are not clear, but probably because of the emphasis on a narrow waistline, especially in women, individuals usually breathe in three different manners: *clavicular, central* and *diaphragmatic.*

Clavicular breathing, as its name suggests, provides for additional space in the thorax during inhalation by noticeable elevation of the upper thorax. Clavicles, sternum and the upper ribs are all lifted rather strenuously and there is little, if any, expansion of the thoracic cavity in the lower extremities via action of the diaphragm. Although, with clavicular breathing, the intake of air is sufficient for speech production, it is undesirable for several reasons. By the elevation of the clavicles and sternum a certain amount of constriction occurs in the laryngeal area preventing the relaxed functioning of the larynx during phonation and probably interfering with potential resonators in this area. Since there has been negligible expansion in the lower thorax, those muscles in this area normally acting to assist in controlled exhalation are incapacitated. Exhalation is, therefore, more abrupt and requires the individual to inhale considerably more times than would otherwise be necessary. The general aesthetic effect of clavicular breathing is usually unfavorable. Sternocleidomastoideus frequently bulges noticeably, gasping during inhalation is often quite audible and, since control is so poor, the general communication impression is sometimes unpleasant to hear as well as to see. Clavicular breathing is quite common among women, quite rare in men.

Central breathing consists of some clavicular activity and some diaphragmatic activity. Although far more efficient for communication effectiveness than clavicular breathing, it does not, however, permit the maximum control necessary for superior speaking. Occasionally, the individual using central breathing will have considerable shortness of breath during a long phrase or sentence and the consequent gasping to accommodate for the shortage is noticeable. Effective conversational speech can be achieved with central breathing; however, projection occasionally is weak during public performances. The majority of women and a small number of men breathe centrally.

Diaphragmatic breathing, as its name suggests, utilizes maximally the services of the diaphragm to increase the volume of the lower thorax during inhalation. As the diaphragm contracts, it flattens pushing down the viscera which in turn bulge forward. There is in diaphragmatic breathing none of the noticeable elevating of the clavicles, tension in the laryngeal area, gasping, and poor control of exhalation. Perhaps the most significant asset of diaphragmatic breathing is the control of expelled air provided by the abdominal muscles mentioned previously. It is usually a requirement for individuals training for professional careers in public speaking or theater to develop diaphragmatic breathing in order to project beyond the footlights.

Although speech scientists may insist on more objective evidence to support the superiority of diaphragmatic breathing, there appears to be sufficient empirical evidence to support the contention.

There is an interesting psychological phenomenon occurring in relation to respiration patterns which should be mentioned here. For unknown reasons, listeners will tend to copy the respiratory pattern of the speaker. Thus, the beginning speech pathologist working with an individual who has severe breathing anomalies as part of his associated symptoms of stuttering behavior will, unless he resists, take on the same breathing pattern as the patient and find himself eventually quite fatigued. This is also true in cases of listening to speakers with noticeable clavicular breathing. An entire audience may become very restless and uncomfortable as the speaker gasps and struggles to provide enough air for the circumstances.

Vital capacity is the maximum volume of air which may be expired following a maximal inspiration. It varies with sex, age, stature, and general physiology. Vital capacity has little or no effect on effective communication. Of course, there must be sufficient air intake for normal phrasing and projection; however, the individual with an extremely high vital capacity is not a better speaker or capable of being one. There is no relationship.

As far as research in the area of respiration is concerned, it seems doubtful whether recent efforts to establish the breathing muscle action sequence in speech is significant. Individual differences are probably much too variable during normal communication circumstances to establish any kind of conclusive data in this respect. It would seem more logical to study in considerable detail the breathing patterns of a group of speakers judged by experts to be superior speakers and compare these data with a group of speakers judged to be inferior speakers. Electromyogram recordings could be utilized; however, simple inspection of the various subjects by trained observers could, it seems, accomplish much.

In concluding this chapter, the beginning student should be reminded once again of the differences between speech breathing and rest breathing. When teaching speech breathing, the differences should be emphasized. Thus, the client should be taught to inhale *with the mouth open*—to mention only one difference.

Chapter 7

PHONATION

PHONATION, AS WE USE IT in this chapter, means sound produced at the vocal folds. To clarify what happens in the larynx to create speech sounds, this chapter begins with a very brief review of the fundamentals of sound production.

In order to have sound of any type, there must be vibration—something must be moving. Vibration results from either one of two physical principles: *inertia* and *elasticity*. Inertia is that property of matter by which matter at rest or in motion remains at rest or in motion unless acted upon by an external force. Elasticity is the tendency of many substances when distorted in shape to resume their original shape. To initiate sound there must be an exciting cause or generator to set the vibrator into motion.

Types of Vibrators

Numerous types of matter are capable of vibrating if set into motion by a generator. Among the most common types are strings (violin), membranes (drum), reeds (oboe), air columns (organs), bars (xylophone), and plates (cymbals).

In the human speech apparatus during phonation the vocal folds forming the margins of the glottis are comparable to the action of strings. During speech reception the tympanic membrane at the entrance into the middle ear is comparable to a drum head as it initiates and transmits sounds to the ossicles. The generator in each case is a stream of air.

Frequency

Frequency refers to the number of times per second (cps) the object is vibrating. In psychological terms it is synonomous with *pitch*. The faster the vibration, the higher the pitch. The rate or speed of vibration is usually determined by the mass, length, and tension of the matter in motion.

Fundamental Frequency

The tone resulting from an object vibrating in its full length is called the fundamental. The fundamental always identifies the pitch of the sound. However, for any object to vibrate only in its full length is rarely found outside the laboratory. Vibrations are usually exceedingly complex being composed of a number of waves (as the object also vibrates in halves or quarters, etc.) blending into what can be called the *tone complex*. Thus a tone is composed not only of the fundamental frequency but also of partials or overtones. To have a harmonious tone complex all the partials must have a common divisor; the common denominator for all being the fundamental frequency. Thus, when the components of a tone complex have frequencies of 400, 600, and 1,000 cps, the fundamental frequency or pitch of the entire tone is perceived as a 200 cps tone. One can experience this quite simply by utilizing a piano. If one strikes a C and E chord, there is harmony because there is a common denominator of the two frequencies generated. If, however, one strikes a C and D chord, there is disharmony because there is no common denominator for the two tones generated. All harmony is based on combinations of partials known to have common denominators.

GENERATION OF SPEECH SOUNDS

The airstream discussed in Chapter 6 is the force or energy necessary to initiate the various speech sounds (phonemes) comprising words. There are three different ways in which air is utilized to generate sounds: *friction, implosion-explosion* and *phonation.*

In friction, for example, during production of the [s] phoneme, the tongue tip usually approximates the upper alveolus medially permitting only a tiny escape of air over the flatted lingual apex. The friction resulting from the impeding of the air in the manner described creates a hissing sound, the [s] phoneme.

In producing the [p] phoneme, air is trapped behind tightly occluded lips which are then abruptly opened resulting in an explosion of air known as the [p] phoneme.

Speech sounds resulting from either friction or implosion-explosion are considered to be in the noise family because they have aperiodic or irregular sound complexes in terms of harmonic combinations. Those phonemes, however, usually described as "voiced"—vowels, for example—are produced by expired air passing over the vocal folds approximated in varying degrees. Voiced sounds have harmonic units and are pleasant to hear. Their production is the only one of the three methods just described to be considered in this chapter.

We have said normal phonation results from expired air passing over approximated vocal folds. There are, reportedly, some obscure African tribes whose members phonate habitually on inspired air during communication—a method quite feasible, however not recommended for use in polite society!

The Larynx

The vocal folds, mentioned previously, are contained within the larynx. The larynx attaches to the trachea inferiorly and to the *hyoid bone* superiorly. (The hyoid bone is thin and U-shaped. Lying in a horizontal position, its legs, called greater cornua or horns, extend posteriorly. In some, the outer surface of the hyoid can be felt through the skin at the junction of the front of the neck and the floor of the mouth. At the point where the greater cornua join the body of the hyoid, there are pointed prominences called the lesser cornua. The hyoid is suspended via the *stylohyoid ligament* which attaches from the temporal bone to the lesser cornua.)

The larynx is composed of cartilages, ligaments and membranes. Its internal parts are moved by intrinsic muscles; the entire larynx is moved by extrinsic muscles.

Cartilages

The larynx contains three single cartilages (*thyroid, cricoid, epiglottis*) and three paired cartilages (*arytenoids, corniculates, cuneiform*).

The *thyroid* cartilage (Fig. 18), the largest cartilage of the larynx, is composed of two lamina fused together at an angle to form a shield-shaped structure. Where the two lamina join there is, especially in males, a prominence commonly called the "Adam's apple." Superiorly and inferiorly at the lateral margins of the thyroid are

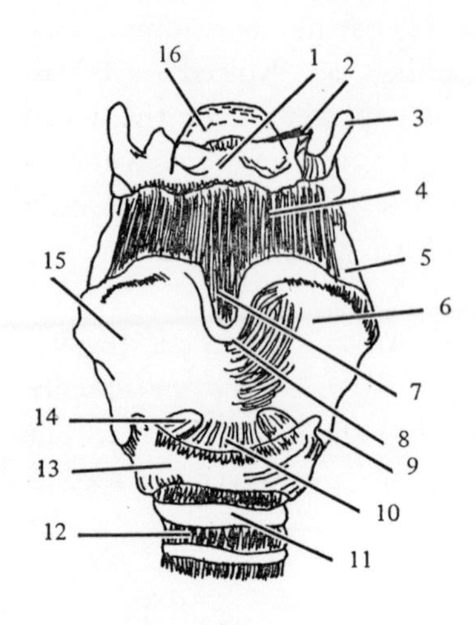

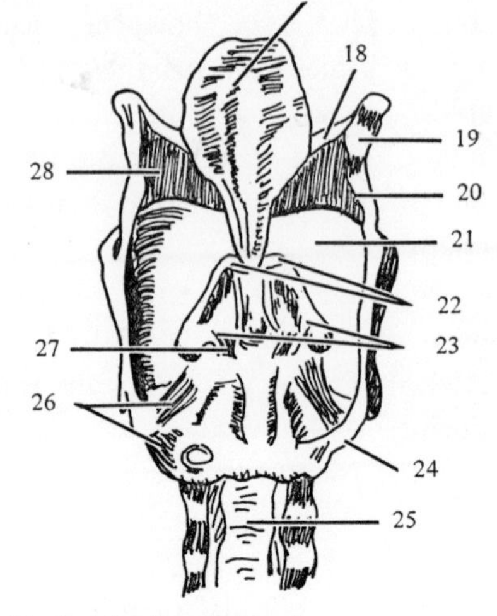

1. Hyoid bone
2. Lesser cornua of the hyoid
3. Greater cornua of the hyoid
4. Thyrohyoid membrane
5. Superior cornua of thyroid
6. Thyroid cartilage lamina
7. Median thyrohyoid ligament
8. Thyroid notch (Adam's apple)
9. Inferior cornua of thyroid
10. Medial cricothyroid ligament
11. Tracheal cartilage
12. Trachea (membranous rings)
13. Cricoid cartilage
14. Conus elasticus
15. Superior thyroid tubercle
16. Epiglottis
17. Epiglottis
18. Hyoid bone
19. Lateral thyrohyoid ligament
20. Superior cornua of thyroid
21. Thyroid cartilage
22. Corniculate cartilage
23. Arytenoid cartilages
24. Inferior cornua of thyroid
25. Trachea
26. Capsular ligament
27. Posterior cricothyroid ligament
28. Thyrohyoid membrane

FIGURE 18. Anterior and posterior views of the larynx.

two sets of cornua. Via the superior cornua, the thyroid attaches to the greater cornua of the hyoid. Inferiorly, the thyroid attaches to the lateral margins of the signet portion of the cricoid cartilage via the inferior cornua.

The *cricoid* cartilage attaches directly to the superior margins of the trachea. Shaped like a signet ring, the signet portion is posterior. The inner surface of the cricoid is continuous with the trachea inferiorly and with the laryngeal cavity superiorly.

The *epiglottis* is shaped like a large leaf with the leafy portion floating freely above the hyoid bone at the root of the tongue. The stem is attached to the thyroid cartilage at the junction of the two lamina.

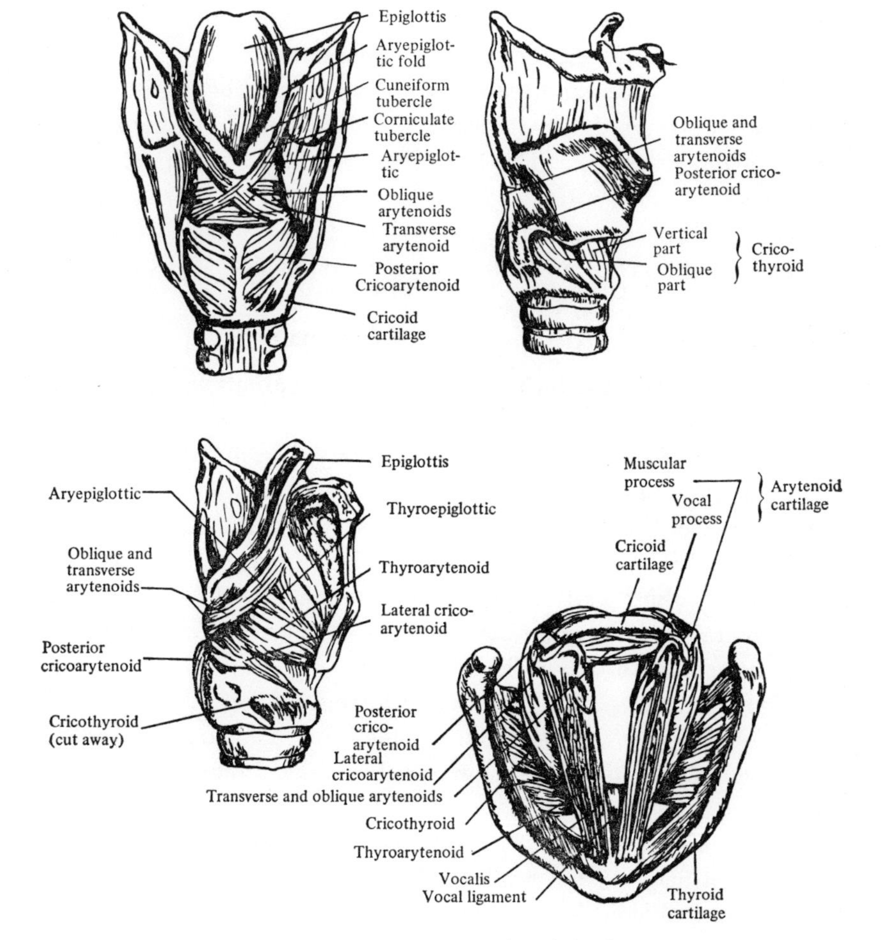

FIGURE 19. The intrinsic muscles of the larynx.

The *arytenoids* are paired. Shaped like irregular pyramids they perch on the posterior and superior margin of the cricoid. The triangular base of each has two processes or projections—a lateral process called the *muscular process* and an anterior process called the *vocal process* (see Fig. 19).

The paired *corniculates* articulate with the arytenoids at their apices, but are actually situated within the *aryepiglottic folds* or *quadrangular membranes*. (The membranous aryepiglottic folds are lateral and anterior projections from the epiglottis above to the medial margins of the arytenoids. Superiorly the folds are widely separated; as they descend, however, they narrow. The terminal, inferior borders are free and thickened and are called the ventricular ligaments. They attach anteriorly at the thyroid notch and posteriorly to the medial border of the arytenoids. The ligaments support what are called the *false vocal folds* or *ventricular folds.*)

The paired *cuneiform* cartilages are also situated in the aryepiglottic fold somewhat anterior and lateral to each arytenoid.

Ligaments and Membranes of the Larynx

The cartilages just described are joined by various ligaments and separated into three divisions by membranes.

The *thyrohyoid membrane* suspends the larynx from the hyoid bone. The membrane attaches superiorly to the upper margins and greater cornua of the hyoid. Passing downward, it terminates upon the superior border and horns of the thyroid cartilage. Medially the membrane is thick and is called the *median thyrohyoid ligament.* Posterolaterally, the membrane becomes ligamentous and connects the greater cornua of the hyoid with the superior horns of the thyroid. This ligament is the *lateral thyrohyoid ligament.*

The *hyoepiglottic ligament* connects the hyoid bone to the epiglottis. The *cricotracheal ligament* connects the cricoid cartilage to the trachea.

The *capsule* and *posterior cricoarytenoid ligament* connect each arytenoid cartilage to the cricoid. The movement permitted at this point of articulation is extensive. The arytenoids are capable of rotating, gliding toward or away from each other as well as tilting forward and downward. The movement here is critical to the opening and closing of the vocal folds as we shall see.

The *capsular ligament* strengthens the joint between the thyroid cartilage and the cricoid where the inferior horns of the thyroid articulate with the lateral margins of the cricoid. The connection here permits the two cartilages to approximate anteriorly.

The *cricothyroid membrane* has a central and paired lateral sections. The central portion, the *medial cricothyroid ligament,* is thickened and acts as a vertical band between the cricoid arch anteriorly and the lower border of the medial portion of the thyroid cartilage. The oblique sections are called the *conus elasticus* or *cricovocal membrane.*

The conus elasticus attaches inferiorly on the superior margins of the arch of the cricoid and extend upward and medially to attach anteriorly at about the lower third of the thyroid lamina at the angle, and posteriorly to the vocal processes of the arytenoid cartilages. The free upper borders of each lateral membrane constitute the *vocal ligaments.*

The *vocal ligaments* extend from the angle of the thyroid anteriorly to the vocal processes of the arytenoids posteriorly. Their inner free edges, covered with a layer of mucous membrane, are thin; the paired thyroarytenoid contained within the conus elasticus has contact with the folds. The edges or lips of the cricothyroid membrane called the conus elasticus thus become the all important vocal folds utilized in phonation.

The *ventricular ligaments,* forming and supporting the *false* or *ventricular vocal folds,* attach anteriorly at the angle of the thyroid above the vocal ligament and posteriorly on the anterolateral surface of the arytenoids at a level higher than the vocal process. The ventriculars are the free margins of the inferior, medial portion of the aryepiglottic fold or quadrangular membrane mentioned previously.

It might be helpful at this point when attempting to visualize the internal aspects of the larynx to think of an hourglass. The top portion of the hourglass is comparable to the aryepiglottic fold or quadrangular membrane curving medially to form the ventricular or false vocal folds. At the point where the sand in the hourglass begins leaving the top portion and enters the lower portion there is a very small portion where the diameter is equal before the sand enters the lower portion. This area is comparable to the space between the false and the true vocal folds called the *ventricle.* The point where the sand begins entering the lower portion of the hourglass is comparable to the true vocal folds; the lower portion to the conus elasticus.

When the vocal folds are open, the space between them is called the *glottis.* The area above the glottis to the entrance into the larynx at the laryngopharynx is called the *hyperglottic cavity* or *vestibule*. The area below the glottis to the entrance into the trachea, the *hypoglottic cavity*. The ventricle—space between the true and false vocal folds—is considered a part of the hyperglottic cavity.

Physiology of the Larynx

Philogenetically the larynx developed as a protective valve against the invasion of food and water into the lungs during the act of swallowing. The protection is provided by three sphincteric mechanisms: *aryepiglottic, true vocal folds,* and the *false vocal folds.*

The *aryepiglottic sphincter,* the most superior, utilizes the fibromuscular lateral folds of the aryepiglottic fold or quadrangular membrane described previously (top portion of the hourglass) to close off the most superior entrance into the larynx. Supported by the cuneiform cartilages the two folds are approximated by action of the aryepiglottic and thyroepiglottic muscles which are extensions respectively of *oblique arytenoideus* and *thyroarytenoideus* discussed later under intrinsic muscles of the larynx.

The *false vocal cord sphincter* occurs when the free margins of the inferior, medial portions of the aryepiglottic folds approximate. Although there is controversy regarding the function of the false cords, structurally, according to Cunningham (1951), the lips of the false folds are so constructed that when approximated they can only prevent air from escaping upward through the laryngeal vestibule. Thus when air pressure is necessary to be built up in the thorax—as in lifting heavy objects—the false cords supply the necessary closure since the true folds because of their structure can impede the air, but apparently cannot prevent air from passing upward. The false cord sphincter is of little or no value in preventing foreign objects from descending into the ventricle. Since muscular fibers from the aryepiglottic folds are capable of bringing the ventriculars together, it appears the false fold sphincter operates independently of the true folds.

The *true vocal fold sphincter* occurs when the free medial edges (vocal folds) of the conus elasticus approximate. The closure prevents any foreign matter which may have penetrated the aryepiglottic sphincter from descending any farther. Most of us have experienced the choking sensation when, during rapid eating, for example, a particle of food is trapped by the true folds. But more important, it is this sphincter which man has learned to utilize for phonation in oral speech; it is the basis for our concern with the larynx.

Muscles of the Larynx

For speech purposes, during forced inhalation the vocal folds are widely separated or fully abducted to enable maximal passageway for the incoming air. For phonation the folds are initially closed or adducted, and then depending on the desired pitch they are additionally tightened, lengthened or partially damped out entirely. This action is accomplished by a group of muscles: the *intrinsic laryngeal muscles.*

The Intrinsics

The *intrinsic muscles of the larynx* are the *posterior cricoarytenoid, lateral cricoarytenoid, cricothyroid, oblique arytenoid, transverse arytenoid, thyroarytenoid* (the deeper fibers of thyroarytenoid are called the *vocalis* and the deeper fibers of vocalis are called the *aryvocalis*), *thyroepiglottic* and *aryepiglottic.* The latter two muscles have already been mentioned in discussing the aryepiglottic sphincter. They are unrelated to phonation. All of the intrinsics are paired with the exception of transverse arytenoid (see Fig. 19).

Innervation of the Intrinsics. With the exception of the cricothyroid muscles, and possibly transverse and oblique arytenoids (interarytenoidei) (Pressman and Kelemen, 1955), innervated by the *superior laryngeal branch of vagus* (C-X), all the remaining intrinsics in this group are innervated by the *recurrent (inferior) laryngeal branch of vagus.* (The interarytenoids are known to be supplied bilaterally by both the right and left recurrent nerves; however, some investigators have reported the interarytenodei do receive fibers from the internal branch of the superior laryngeal nerves and therefore have a double motor innervation).

The *posterior cricoarytenoids* attach from the posterior surface of the cricoid cartilage to the muscular process of the arytenoids. Their action rotates the vocal processes of the arytenoids outward thus opening, or abducting, the folds. These are the only muscles which act to open the glottis.

The *lateral cricoarytenoids* attach anteriolaterally to the cricoid and to the muscular process of the arytenoids. Their action pulls the arytenoids forward and also rotates the vocal processes inward thus tensing the folds and closing them.

The *cricothyroids* have two parts. The anteriomedial portion running almost vertically attaches from the superior border of the cricoid arch to the inferior margins of the thyroid. The posterior part also attaches at the cricoid arch but runs laterally and posteriorly attaching to the inferior cornu of the thyroid. Their action draws the thyroid forward and down and elevates the arch of the cricoid; it elongates the vocal folds, making them tense if the arytenoids are fixed. They also assist in adducting the folds.

The *oblique arytenoids* attach from the base of one arytenoid to the apex of the opposite arytenoid. Their action closes the vocal folds.

Transverse arytenoid attaches along the muscular process and lateral border of one arytenoid and crosses over to attach to the lateral margins of the opposite arytenoid. Its action draws the arytenoids together and adducts the folds.

The *thyroarytenoid muscles,* including what are called the internal muscular fibers, *vocalis* and *aryvocalis,* attach from the internal, inferior surface of the angle of the thyroid cartilage to the vocal process and anterolateral surface of the base of the arytenoids at the muscular process. Vocalis is thought to form the main, medial mass of the vocal folds and is closely related to the lateral portions of the vocal ligament. Aryvocalis refers to the deepest and shortest fibers of the entire thyroarytenoid mass running from and into the vocal ligament. (As we shall see in examining various theories of vocal fold function, the tenability of Husson's neuromuscular theory depends on the insertion of the muscle fibers of the thyroarytenoids not parallel with the vocal folds, but at right angles, like the teeth of a comb, in a highly complicated pattern.)

The effect of the action of the thyroarytenoids has not been entirely established; however, the various divisions of the entire mass apparently act separately to make various adjustments along the margins of the vocal folds during pitch changes. Thus, portions of the folds may be relaxed, shortened or tensed (not, however, by elongation, but probably by diagonal pull); portions may be entirely damped out.

Extrinsic Laryngeal Muscles

The extrinsic laryngeal muscles, as their name suggests, are attached to the larynx in such a manner their action moves the entire larynx rather than parts of it. They can be divided into two groups. The *infrahyoids* (*sternohyoid, thyrohyoid, omohyoid,* and *sternothyroid*) all have attachments readily identifiable by their names. As a group they are generally related to depression of the entire larynx.

The *suprahyoids* (*digastric, stylohyoid, mylohyoid, geniohyoid,* and *hypoglossus*) as a group are most active during swallowing when the entire larynx is elevated.

Electromyographic investigations of the action of the extrinsics during the phonation of individual vowels and during rising pitch have reported different electrical activity for similar muscles. One investigation reported pronounced electrical activity in the sternothyroid muscles during phonation with low and high pitch, while there was a decrease in electrical activity in the middle of the tone scale. Another investigation found increasing activity in the sternothyroid muscle with rising pitch, the activity growing evenly through the full tone scale from low to high pitch (K. Faaborg-Anderson, 1965).

During phonation it would appear logical to suspect the extrinsics to be related far more to the shaping of the various cavities (especially the oral cavity) for the resonation of the desired vowel than to the actual phonation of the vowel; thus these muscles should probably be considered best as muscles related to resonation rather than phonation.

All of the suprahyoids, except stylohyoid, are related to jaw and tongue movements during the articulation of various speech sounds. During forced inspiration, the sternothyroid muscle reportedly showed pronounced electrical activity; the thyrohyoid muscle showed pronounced electrical activity during inspiration.

Pitch

Phonation, as we have described it, cannot be separated from pitch or the frequency (number of cycles per second) of the sound initiated at the vocal folds. Voiceless or unphonated phonemes also have pitch; however they will be considered in the chapter on resonation.

To have sound of any kind we must have vibration. In order to initiate vibration there must be a generator or acting force. Thus the airstream passes over vocal folds in various stages of adduction and in a manner much like holding two sheets of paper together and blowing over their free edges (Bernoueli effect) the folds seem to be sucked together as they appear to wave much like a flag in a brisk breeze. The pitch produced by the movements is determined by the length, tension, elasticity, mass and shape of the vocal folds, or margins along the glottis. Using the muscles previously described any part of the glottis can be closed or opened without necessarily relating to any other part.

Optimum Pitch

Each adult because of his peculiar laryngeal anatomy has an optimum or best pitch around which his speaking range will cluster. For those who can sing well enough, optimum pitch may usually be determined with good accuracy by having the individual sing down the scale to the lowest tone comfortably sustained. By then singing up the scale five semitones (black and white keys on the piano), the optimum pitch is located. For those who cannot carry a tune, a vocalized sigh very often proves quite satisfactory. (In cases of severe dysphonia only a qualified speech pathologist should make decisions about optimum pitch.)

There is a constant change in pitch from birth to death. At birth the vocal folds are 3 millimeters long; at fifteen years, approximately 9.5 millimeters. The biggest change occurs at puberty when the folds in the female elongate from 12.5 to 17 millimeters and in males from 17 to 23 millimeters. Pitch change, it should be noted, does not always coincide with other physical changes at puberty.

Although optimum pitch for females seems to be dropping somewhat if one considers female entertainers and college women as a representative sample, in the past, optimum pitch for females was usually considered to be approximately 256 cps (middle C on the piano); for men, one octave lower, or 128 cps.

Individuals with low-pitched voices usually have long and relatively broad vocal folds. High-pitched voices usually have short and relatively narrow vocal folds.

Range refers to the extent of pitches the individual is capable of producing comfortably from the lowest to the highest. Trained speakers usually are capable of utilizing 1½ octaves and usually vary their pitch changes within that range. Trained singers, on the other hand, cover three octaves and the greatest have been noted for the wide range of their voices. Caruso, it has been reported, suffered from chronic laryngitis which apparently contributed to the edematus and rounded condition of his vocal folds. To what extent his great range in the high registers was related to the peculiar condition of his folds makes for interesting speculation.

With age, ossification of the various cartilages occurs. In some, ossification begins by age twenty-five. By age sixty-five it is thought that most of the cartilages have ossified, thus frequently accounting for the gradual loss of range in singers and for the monotone of old age.

How Pitch Changes

We have just been discussing the various pitch changes associated with maturation and finally with the aging process. There is another kind of pitch change, however, used constantly in oral speech. It is usually called *inflection* if the pitch change occurs within the same syllable; *interval* if the change occurs between neighboring syllables. Both are used for emphasis, variety, and to express shades of meanings. What happens during the pitch changes is thought to be as follows.

Given a set of vocal folds of a certain length, to raise the pitch the folds would be stretched (decreasing the vibrating cross section) and stiffened (increasing the overall tautness and speed of vibration). The deepened pitch of the patient with laryngitis or polypoid thickening of the folds is due to an increase of the vibrating cross-section of the cords by inflammatory swelling, or tissue growth.

When the higher notes are reached (this would be true largely for singers or to achieve certain vocal effects) the thyroid is tilted forward, the folds are stretched farther and their inner margins are sharpened to a narrow angle. Vibration is limited to the inner margins, and the increased stiffness of the folds prevents extensive vibration. In producing still higher pitches (high soprano and falsetto) damping occurs. The posterior portion of the folds remain in close approximation, but are damped out with only the anterior portion of the folds vibrating. Thus, in addition to the stretching and thickening, we now also have less overall area increasing speed of vibration. Vocalis and aryvocalis muscles are thought to be considerably involved in making the adjustments necessary to produce high pitches.

Most classical concepts of phonation, with slight variations regarding which muscles are involved in pitch changes, can generally be included in what has been described above. Husson's neuromuscular, or neurochronaxic, theory is sharply different.

Husson's neuromuscular theory roots in a publication in 1950 by a German anatomist (Goerttler) in which it was reported that serial dissection of the muscle fibers of the vocal folds showed them not to run parallel with the free margins, but to insert like the teeth of a comb in a complicated pattern into the ligaments at the margins of the folds.

On the basis of this report Husson postulated that the opening phase of the vibratory cycle of the folds is an active process due to contractions of thyroarytenoideus. The recurrent nerve can, Husson claims, transmit up to 500 impulses per second. For higher frequencies he assumes the fibers of the vocal muscle are stimulated and contract in relays permitting "biphasic" vibrations up to 1000 cps, and still higher frequencies to occur by triphasic stimulation.

Husson's theory has been attacked by many. Neurophysiologists question the feasibility of the biphasic and triphasic action described by Husson. And if this portion of his proposal is untenable, as we are led to suspect, the entire neuromusculartheory must be discarded, for muscles, it is known, cannot be stimulated at rapid enough rates to account for pitches above 500 cps without becoming spastic.

It should also be noted in evaluating Husson's theory that usable voice has been reported in patients with bilateral recurrent nerve paralysis with the folds in the adducted position.

Positions of the Folds in Health and Disease

The vocal folds, or the margins of the glottis, have variable positions depending on the activity (in health) or partial or lack of activity (in disease).

Median. The folds are adducted in the midline. Position is also called phonatory and midline.

Glottic Chink. Folds are adducted, but slack permits minimal separation during respiration.

Paramedian. Folds lie slightly to the side of the midline. If both are paralyzed, they are separated posteriorly by a distance of 3.5 or 4 millimeters.

Cadaveric. Folds lie in a position between paramedian and gentle abduction. Folds are slack and in the same position as they assume in the cadaver.

Gentle Abduction. Folds are abducted farther than in the cadaveric position, but not fully. This is the position during quiet respiration.

Full Abduction. Folds are abducted to their fullest; glottis is at its widest. This is the position during forced inspiration when maximum intake of air is desired.

Whispering. Anterior, two thirds of the folds are adducted; posterior, one third are open.

The research in the area of phonation in America has been scant. Most of the work in relation to the intrinsic and extrinsic muscles of the larynx has been conducted by European otolaryngologists. In America, otolaryngologists are in such small supply few apparently have sufficient time or motivation to conduct investigations or even to report clinical cases of interest to speech pathologists. An interesting effort has been made by Dr. Moses (Moses, 1954) to relate vocal pathologies (including many pitch disorders) to psychic disturbances of various kinds. Thinking back to the discussion of the nervous system—especially the autonomic—it is not difficult to relate anxiety states to numerous disorders of phonation.

Organic pathologies of the folds or larynx have been described in the literature quite frequently. Paralysis of the vocal folds, nodules, contact ulcers, carcinoma of the larynx are fairly well known types of cases discussed in every general work on speech pathology. We need much more information about such cases in order to plan suitable remediation.

The most challenging area for investigation, it seems, is the relationship between various emotional attitudes and phonation. With the exception of paralysis and carcinoma the vast majority of phonation pathologies seem to be related to misuse of phonation—pitch too high, too low (often resulting in nodules or contact ulcers respectively). Although some recent data suggest a relationship between neuropathology and psychophonasthenia, hysterical symptoms of all types are very often revealed at the level of phonation.

Personality dynamics are extremely difficult to quantify and to study. To attempt to relate them to phonation—a variable in itself—is attempting to relate two variable variables. But the challenge remains.

A much closer relationship between experienced teachers of singing and speech pathologists might be very beneficial. Phonation is of the utmost importance to professional singers. The disparity between singing and speaking seems so slight that a great deal might be learned by pooling information. Or perhaps all speech pathologists in training should be required to take singing lessons!

Chapter 8

RESONATION

IN THE FINAL ANALYSIS, both the identity and pleasantness of a tone depends to a great extent on resonation. The original sound phonated at the vocal folds is quite weak in intensity, colorless and difficult to identify. The resonators—cavities and sounding boards—through which the sound passes enroute to the external air, supply the amplification of various frequencies within each tone-complex providing increased intensity, color (quality) and identity.

WHAT RESONATION IS

Resonation is related to vibrations of two basic types—vibration of matter and vibration (pulsations) of air within a cavity. Some basic physical principles may help to clarify how resonation is related to speech sound production.

A vibrating body has a frequency at which it vibrates at greatest ease called its *natural* or *free* period. Whenever matter is set into motion, its natural tendency, therefore, is to vibrate at its natural frequency. Whatever initiates the original movement is called the *exciting cause.* If I pluck a violin string, the string will vibrate at its natural frequency (depending on the tension and mass of the string at that particular moment). My fingers are, in this case, the exciting cause.

If, in the example mentioned above, the string set into vibration was not stretched across the wooden cavity comprising the major structure of the instrument, but merely extended between two wooden pegs, when plucked, the sound would be dull, lacking in intensity and identifiability. The string, however, would continue to vibrate for a longer period of time than if it were stretched across the wooden body of a violin. What happens is related to resonation. In both instances the strength with which the string is plucked is reflected in the resulting tone—the greater the energy originally supplied the louder the resulting tone. However, in the case where the string is stretched over the wooden cavity (which acts as a sounding board as well as a cavity resonator) the energy initiated by the exciting cause is absorbed and radiated more rapidly through the wood, the air in the cavity is set into motion, and the tone produced sounds louder, richer, and has clearer identity (less sharp or flat). The wooden case has supplied no new energy; what happens is the result of resonation.

In some instances, a resonator may act as the exciting cause. In the case of the violin previously mentioned, if a tone of high frequency is elicited by it, quite possibly a very thin glass goblet on a nearby shelf may begin vibrating. This is called *sympathetic* vibration. The goblet, it should be noted, will continue to vibrate until all its energy has been dissipated although the tone originally produced by the violin has terminated.

Since air has elasticity and mass, it is a permanent means for transmitting sound pulsations. When the goblet mentioned above began to vibrate sympathetically, the pulsations of air initiated by the violin string were transmitted to the area where the goblet stood. Because the natural frequency of the glass was the same or very close to a frequency transmitted, it responded by vibrating, thus causing the air within the goblet to pulsate.

Since air surrounds us constantly, all sounds, it can be seen, are automatically resonated. Not all resonation, however, is beneficial. Only if the natural frequency of a vibrating body is identical or very close to the natural frequencies (there may be more than one) of the resonator, is the tuning said to be *sharp*. When a potential resonator is not naturally in tune with the vibrating body it may be forced into vibration. In such instances, however, the resulting tone may have a frequency somewhere between the frequencies of the vibrating body and resonator.

Damping may destroy the original sound entirely. The absence of resonators friendly to the original tone plus absorbent texture of surfaces in which the sound circulates will produce the damping effect.

Musical instruments are constructed with principles of resonation in mind. The cavity texture and size of the instruments are fashioned to possess their own, more or less, natural periods capable of reproducing only sounds of definite pitch and quality. An oboe, for example, sounds quite differently than a clarinet. The exciting cause in both instruments is an air stream vibrating a wooden reed: the pitch and quality differences are caused by differences in the structure of the resonators.

Cavities as Resonators

As we have said previously, air has elasticity and mass; it is the amount of air within a cavity that is critical to the pulsations of air in and out of that cavity. The volume of the cavity, therefore, must be considered. The greater the volume of a cavity, the longer will be the time required for pressure differences to equalize. The larger the cavity, the slower the rate of pulsations or vibrations.

A natural consequence of what has just been said is related to the size of the opening into the cavity. A large opening permits more rapid pulsations and a more rapid equalization of pressure within the cavity.

The texture of the surfaces of the cavity are very important to the tones resonated by the cavity. Sharp, hard textures are known to be friendly to high frequencies. A shrill or metallic quality often results from hard surfaces. Soft, absorbent textures are considered desirable for broadcasting studios because of their friendliness to lower overtones considered more desirable acoustically by the average listener.

Surfaces as Resonators

Any matter is capable of some vibration; however, some matter is far more suitable for vibration than others. The violin is an example not only of cavity resonation, but also of surface or sounding board resonation. The famous Stradivarius violins achieved their world acclaim because of the wood used in their construction. Antonio Stradivari apparently used some obscure technique in constructing, polishing and finishing the wood used in the body of the Stradivarius. The result, apparently, was a remarkable resiliency of the wood adding great beauty to the tone complex.

A banjo is more dependent on sounding-board resonation than the violin since its head is entirely open, minimizing the effect of cavity resonation. The banjo has a membranous surface capable of a wide range of vibrations.

Sounding-board resonation may be demonstrated by placing a vibrating tuning fork on a desk top. The tone upon contact with the desk will be amplified and may be enriched as the desk top is forced into vibration, thus adding to the total amount of energy produced by the fork. It should be noted that without contacting the desk top the sound produced by the fork may be quite weak, but it will have a longer duration since the energy is not dissipated as rapidly.

Coupling

When several resonators are connected and operate as one system, they are said to be coupled. Coupling usually refers to a system of connected cavities; however, a sounding board may be coupled to a cavity. Many musical instruments have coupled resonators. In a coupled system where the effect of one part is great on a second or third, the system may be said to be *tightly* coupled; if there is little effect of one part on another, it is *loosely* coupled.

POTENTIAL RESONATORS

On the basis of what has just been discussed, the speech apparatus, it appears, lends itself remarkably well to resonating the sounds phonated at the level of the vocal folds. The following potential human resonators should be considered in evaluating resonation phenomena in the production of speech:

1. Tracheobronchial tree
   a. Lungs
   b. Treachea and bronchi
   c. Sternum, clavicles and rib cage
2. Laryngeal cavities
   a. Hypoglottal cavity
   b. Hyperglottal cavity
3. Pharyngeal cavity
   a. Nasopharynx
   b. Oropharynx
   c. Laryngopharynx

4. Oral cavity
5. Nasal cavity
6. Sinuses

Tracheobronchial Tree

The anatomy of this region was discussed in relation to respiration and will need no further elaboration here. In considering the lungs as resonators, the question to be asked at this point is whether their spongy tissue has any effect on the absorption or damping of a tone. Since there is a great deal of subdividing of the various tubes passing from the trachea into the lungs, it seems extremely doubtful that the lungs would have any effect on the original sound phonated, or that the portion of the tracheobronchial tree inferior to the trachea has any effect on the tone complex. Although very debatable, it is logical to argue that the trachea may have some resonating effect. There is no reason why the sound initiated at the vocal folds cannot travel down before it travels up, thus passing through the trachea.

The function of the sternum, clavicles and rib cage as sounding boards is also debatable. The sensation of vibrations in the chest area, especially when tones of lower frequencies are emitted, is a common experience to many male speakers. Some speech teachers apparently believe the chest area has significant sounding-board potential, for they frequently ask the student who is working toward developing a richer quality to place his hand on his chest to encourage the development of vibratory sensations in that area.

At least some tones, it seems logical to suspect, are transmitted to the bony areas of the body near the source of the sound. The sternum, clavicles, and rib cage probably can be considered sounding boards. Whether the sounds resonated are transmitted from the vocal folds internally, or whether they reach the chest area after leaving the oral and nasal cavities to be transmitted externally via the air should provide for an interesting academic discussion.

Laryngeal Cavities

The *hypoglottal* cavity (Chap. 7) is the most inferior portion of the larynx between the glottis and the trachea. The shape and position of the hypoglottal cavity is constantly varying as different vowels are produced at different pitches. (This can be experienced by phonating several vowels at different pitches while touching the larynx lightly with the fingers.) Thus it seems the hypoglottal cavity probably is related to resonation, at least in a minor way. This area is quite small in comparison with the oral, pharyngeal and nasal cavities. Its influence must be minimal.

The *hyperglottal* cavity extends from the glottis to the hyoid bone. Actually this area can be thought of as two cavities—the portion above the ventricular folds and the portion below them. The portion below the ventriculars probably acts as a resonator in much the same way as the hypoglottal cavity. The portion above, and the ventriculars themselves, can logically be considered a source of considerable harsh quality if excessive tension causes thickening and partial approximating of them, thus impeding the air stream and creating sharp surface textures friendly to high overtones. (In discussing various types of speech breathing the relation between clavicular breathing, laryngeal tension and harshness has been previously mentioned.)

The effect of the epiglottis on resonation in the hyperglottal cavity has been questioned. Since the epiglottis is cartilaginous, when excessive tension occurs in this area surface tension can act to transmit high frequencies and constriction to narrow the general passageway. The normal shape and position of the epiglottis suggests that it must have some effect on resonation, acting probably primarily as a sounding board. However, its effect appears minimal.

Pharyngeal Cavity

The pharyngeal cavity extends from the base of the skull to the level of the sixth cervical vertebra and the inferior border of the cricoid cartilage where it opens into the esophagus. Composed of muscles and membranes, it is generally considered as three separate cavities: *nasopharynx, oropharynx,* and *laryngopharynx.*

The *nasopharynx* is directly behind the nose and extends from the base of the skull superiorly to the level of the soft palate inferiorly. The cavity is always open and communicates with the nasal cavities through the choanae. On the posterior wall is a mass of lymphoid tissue, the *pharyngeal tonsil,* commonly called *adenoids.* The two posterior choanae mark the most superior point of the anterior wall of the pharynx. The two choanae are separated by the posterior margin of the nasal septum.

The *Eustachian tubes* enter the naropharynx about the level of the inferior turbinates (see Fig. 20-2). Extending upward, backward and outward, each tube opens into the anterior wall of the middle ear behind the tympanic membrane. Osseous near the membrane and cartilaginous toward the pharynx, the mucous membrane lining of the tubes is continuous with that of the pharynx and the tympanic membrane. Since the Eustachian tubes are the means for equalizing air pressure changes between the external environment and the middle ear, the sensation of the ears closing and then suddenly seeming to pop open is common during sudden ascents and descents.

The *oropharynx* extends from the soft palate to the level of the hyoid bone. It opens into the oral cavity at the isthmus faucium. The *palatine tonsils* are in the lateral walls between the faucial pillars.

The *laryngopharynx* extends from the hyoid bone to the inferior border of the cricoid cartilage where it becomes continuous with the esophagus.

Muscles Related to Pharyngeal Cavities

Because the pharyngeal cavities are capable of a considerable variety of change either in volume, shape or surface texture, they are of primary importance for resonation. Changes are accomplished by the following constrictor muscles of the pharynx: *superior pharyngeal constrictor, middle pharyngeal constrictor,* and the *inferior pharyngeal constrictor.*

In general the constrictor fibers are flat and insert into the median raphe on the posterior part of the pharynx. The raphe is formed by the interlacing of the tendinous fibers of the muscles of the opposite side. It extends inferiorly from the pharyngeal tubercle of the occipital bone. The constrictors overlap each other. The origin of each constrictor is as follows: *superior*: palate bone, internal pterygoid plate, pterygomandibular ligament, alveolar process of jaw and side of tongue; *middle*: cornua of hyoid bone and stylohyoid ligament; *inferior*: cricoid and thyroid cartilages. All are innervated by the pharyngeal plexus formed by branches from C-IX, pharyngeal branch of C-X and from superior cervical ganglion of the sympathetic system. The action of the constrictors is to contract the pharynx as in swallowing.

Several additional muscles of the pharynx are related to changes in the cavities. *Stylopharyngeus* raises and dilates the pharynx and *salpingopharyngeus* narrows the fauces. When the velopharyngeal closure is discussed a bit later, it should also be noted that *pharyngopalatinus* and *glossopalatinus,* comprising the faucial pillars, should be included in the group of muscles involved in changing the various aspects of the pharynx.

When singing teachers ask their pupils to work for "an open throat" they may not always be able to identify the area they are talking about. However, most, it seems, consider the pharynx as the throat. The "openness" is probably associated with relaxed surfaces and minimal constriction of those portions of the pharynx capable of constriction (laryngopharynx and oropharynx). The nasopharynx is incapable of little if any change; however, surface texture must be considered for this portion of the pharynx. By voluntarily tightening the pharynx and then singing a vowel it is quite easy to experience the effect constriction and excessive tension will have on the tone. The metallic, harsh quality resulting suggests that narrowing of the cavity along with the tightening of the cavity walls has reenforced only high partials, ignoring the lower, enriching ones almost entirely.

Many professional singers have reported how their singing teachers encouraged them to think of many tones as "coming out of the top of their heads" or "from behind their eyes." Unfortunately they were never told why. Perhaps, in cases of sopranos and tenors, the object was to incorporate use of the bones of the skull as sounding boards. In any event, many singers do think of placing tones high in the pharynx. Apparently this does influence the pleasantness of the sounds produced.

On the basis of what has just been said, the pharynx is, apparently, considered vitally important to successful singing. Whether it is just as important to successful speaking has yet to be demonstrated. Logically, however, it appears to be of major importance to pleasant voice quality.

Oral Cavity

The mouth constitutes the oral cavity. Since the anatomy of the oral cavity is usually associated more easily with the articulation of speech sounds, it will be discussed in detail in the chapter which follows.

The oral cavity may be considered as a single resonator or as a multiple resonator. When the tongue lies flat on the floor of the mouth and the lips and teeth are open, there is a single resonator as in the production of the [*a*] sound. When the tongue divides the cavity connecting them only by a small opening, as in the production of the [i] sound, it is a multiple resonator.

There are other possible subdivisions within the oral cavity; between the dorsum of the tongue and the palate, between the tongue and the teeth or lips, between the teeth and lips, and between the teeth and cheeks.

One needs only to attempt to produce any vowel without opening the teeth and lips to appreciate the importance of the oral cavity as a resonator. To experience how changing one exit from the oral cavity will effect resonation, one needs only to say "How are you?" with lips only partially open as if mumbling, followed by lips moving normally.

One can also experience the audible effect of surface texture changes within the oral cavity by voluntarily constricting the posterior portion of the oral cavity by drawing the cheeks in tightly and by tensing the lower jaw while producing any vowel. The harsh, metallic quality resulting from the tightening of the surface should be apparent.

Singing teachers stress the importance of a relaxed jaw and open and rounded lips (for most vowels) to effective resonation. Both, on the basis of observation, also appear essential for effective oral speech resonation.

The Nose

The nose can probably be understood best by thinking of it as having two major divisions: the *external* nose (the visible portion, usually thought of as the nose) and the *internal* nose (the invisible, nasal cavity). Both divisions are formed by the fusion of several bones and cartilages (see Fig. 20-1).

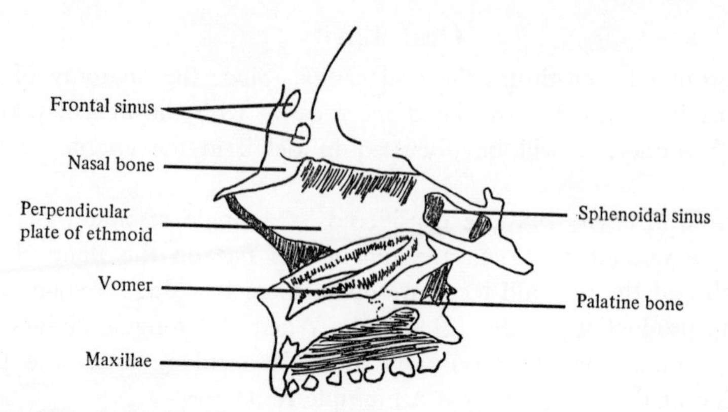

FIGURE 20-1. Sagittal section showing sinuses and bones related to nasal cavity.

The external nose is composed of the nasal bones which produce the bridge of the external nose and the frontal processes of the maxillary bones which form the lateral portions of the external nose as well as the major framework for the cheeks.

The cartilages forming the external nose consist of the *cartilage of the nasal septum,* the paired *lateral nasal cartilages,* and the paired *major* (greater) *alar cartilages.*

The cartilage of the nasal septum is the visible portion of the external nose dividing it into right and left nostrils. The cartilage fuses posteriorly with the ethmoid bone and superiorly with the nasal bones and lateral cartilages. Inferiorly and medially it meets the medial crura of the major alar cartilages. (The nasal septum, it should be noted, is the partition between both divisions of the nose; it is cartilagenous in the external nose, but formed by the fusion of several bones in the nasal cavity.) In more than 50 per cent of the population there is a deviation of the nasal septum. Extensive deviation may occlude one side of the nose partially or completely.

The lateral nasal cartilages attach superiorly to the nasal bones and to the frontal processes of the maxillary bones. Inferiorly they fuse with the major alar cartilages.

The major alar cartilages are thin and flexible and shape both the medial and lateral portions of the nostrils (*medial* and *lateral crura*). Medially the central post dividing the nostrils is called the *columella.* The columella along with the medial crura and the adjacent soft tissue are all movable. Their mobility is demonstrated by inspection;

however during animated conversation this movable area will frequently reflect attitudes of all kinds.

There are several small muscles of the external nose; however, they are unimportant to the oral speech process.

The internal nose or nasal cavity consists of a large general cavity extending from the floor of the cranium superiorly to the roof of the mouth inferiorly. The bony nasal septum divides the cavity into two *nasal fossae.* Laterally are the *nasal conchae* (turbinates) superior, middle, and inferior. The middle and superior conchae are light, shelf-like, spongy processes from the lateral mass of the ethmoid bone. Inferiorly, an independent bone projects shelf-like forming the inferior concha (see Fig. 20-2).

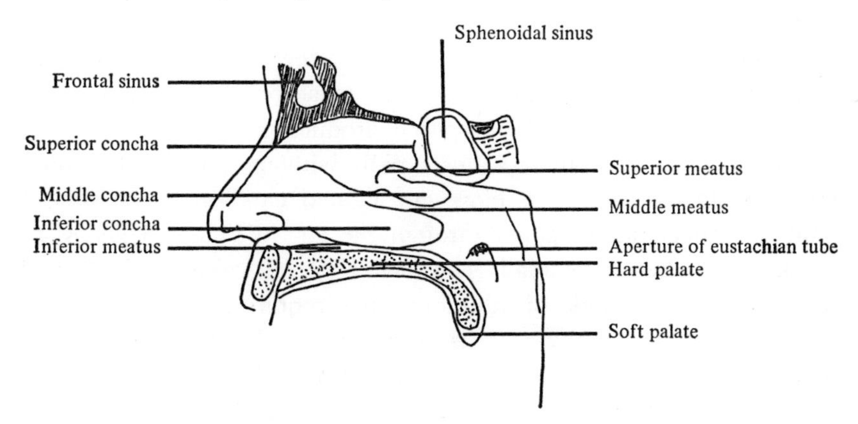

FIGURE 20-2. Lateral wall of nasal cavity.

The conchae incompletely divide each fossa into three passageways lying directly beneath each concha—the *superior middle,* and *inferior meati.* Each fossa may thus be divided into a vestibule, lying just inside the nostrils, the spheno-ethmoidal recess above the superior concha and the superior, middle and inferior meatuses lying underneath the superior, middle and inferior concha, respectively (see Fig. 20).

Each fossa communicates with the nasopharynx posteriorly via the *choanae;* anteriorly with the air via the nostrils. The entire fossa is lined with mucous membrane richly supplied with blood vessels. The endings of the olfactory nerve lie in the mucosa in the region above the superior concha. The facial nerve sends motor fibers to the blood vessels and glands. Trigeminal supplies nasal glands and blood vessels.

Vasomotor nerves may produce immediate effects upon the diameter of the nasal passages and the sinuses. Since anger may quickly produce swelling of the mucosa, and fear shrink them, the nose has long been considered significant in emotional behavior of all kinds. German psychiatrists have been especially concerned with what they considered "the nasal neurosis."

As air enters the nose, the fine hairs at the entrance to the nostrils screen out grosser particles of foreign matter. As it passes along, the air is warmed and takes up moisture from the mucous secreted by many mucous glands. The ciliary activity of the epithelium removes finer dust particles.

Important as the nose is, there are occasions when it is necessary to partition it off temporarily in order to accomplish certain goals, both for life purposes and for speech production.

To enable us to swallow water rapidly without some of it coming out through our noses, to blow out lighted candles, to yawn and pant, to propel bits of paper through the air, to inflate balloons, to speak with what is generally considered "good voice quality" and to perform a multitude of additional acts requiring an excursion of air through the oral cavity, it is necessary for the nasopharynx and nasal cavities to be rendered inactive, or partially inactive. This is accomplished by what is called the velopharyngeal closure.

The Velopharyngeal Closure

The closure between the nose and the mouth is made by the elevation and tension of the velum (soft palate) to extend posteriorly to the pharyngeal wall approximately at the point where it bulges forward slightly.

The soft palate attaches anteriorly to the hard palate and laterally to the walls of the pharynx. A thin, strong aponeurosis supports the muscles and provides substance to the soft palate. The palatine aponeurosis attaches to the hard palate and is continuous laterally with the pharyngeal aponeurosis. Although the velum is frequently considered synonymous with the soft palate, it is sometimes considered as the most posterior portion of the soft palate that hangs down like a partially closed curtain. The pharynx has been discussed earlier in this chapter.

Muscles Related to the Velopharyngeal Closure

The following muscles of the palate are involved in making a closure: *tensor veli palatini, levator veli palatini, musculus uvulae, glossopalatinus,* and *pharyngopalatinus.*

Tensor Veli Palatini. This muscle attaches from the spine of the sphenoid bone, lateral surface of the cartilaginous portion of the eustachian tubes; descends along the outer surface of the internal pytergoid plate and, becoming tendenous, bends at right angles around the hamulus. It inserts into the posterior border of the palatal bone and the aponeurosis of the soft palate.

Innervated by the mandibular branch of C-V, the action of one of the paired muscles will draw the velum to one side. Both muscles acting together will stretch the velum.

Levator Veli Palatini. This muscle attaches from the under surface of the apex of the hard portion of the temporal bone and from the cartilaginous portion of the eustachian tube. Descending obliquely, it inserts into the aponeurosis of the soft palate. Paired, it is innervated by C-X. Its action elevates the velum.

Musculus Uvulae. This muscle attaches from the aponeurosis of the soft palate. Fibers pass posteriorly and downward into the mucous membrane of the uvula forming the greater portion of the uvula. It is frequently paired. (The uvula is cone-shaped and of variable size, projecting downward from the center of the lower border of the velum. May be abnormally long and act as a foreign body in the pharynx.) Innervated by C-X, its action raises the uvula and shortens it.

Glossopalatinus. This paired muscle forms the anterior pillars of the fauces. (The fauces form a port between the mouth and the pharynx. They are bounded superiorly by the velum, inferiorly by the root of the tongue.) Glossopalatinus attaches from the under surface of the aponeurosis of the soft palate. It descends in the anterior pillars of the fauces and inserts into the sides of the tongue. Innervated by C-X, its action elevates the posterior portion of the tongue, draws the sides of the velum down constricting the isthmus of the fauces.

Pharyngopalatinus. This muscle attaches from the aponeurosis of the soft palate, the posterior margins of the hard palate, and the lower portion of the cartilage of the eustachian tubes. Paired, it extends into the posterior pillars of the fauces and inserts into the posterior border of the thyroid cartilage and the aponeurosis of the pharynx. Innervated by C-X, its action elevates the larynx and pharynx, narrows the fauces and depresses soft palate.

In addition to the muscles of the palate just mentioned, the action of the *superior pharyngeal constrictor,* discussed earlier, assists in narrowing the opening between the pharynx and the velum. Through its action the pharynx bulges forward slightly at a point known as Passavant's cushion at the lower margin of the nasopharynx. (The cushion is formed by contraction of muscle fibers coursing around the pharynx from the palate in a horizontal direction. The fibers are thought to be part of the pharyngopalatinus muscle which has fused posteriorly with the superior constrictor muscle.) Other pharyngeal muscles are thought by some to be involved.

Although only three phonemes, [m], [n], and [ŋ] are normally resonated exclusively in the nasopharynx and nasal cavity, most speakers fail to make a complete velopharyngeal closure during the production of the remaining phonemes either by accident or design. In certain areas of the United States nasal resonance of certain vowels, produced orally in other areas, typifies the speech of the natives. The French language is highly nasal. Many voice and diction coaches encourage some nasal resonation on all vowels believing it increases the "warmth" of the quality. In any event, it seems more realistic to consider the amount of nasal resonation present in speech rather than its total presence or absence.

As a resonator, the nasal cavity must be considered important. Communicating directly as it does with the nasopharynx, it is part of a system coupled with the entire pharynx. The absorbant nature of the conchae suggest that some nasal resonance may indeed "warm" the tones (by eliminating high frequency accents) in much the same way as thick carpets and cloth-covered walls are used in sound studios.

During a heavy head cold, or sometimes during highly emotional behavior, the cul-de-sac effect on resonation (hyponasality) is immediately apparent. The swollen and congested mucous membrane lining of the nose prevents the free transmission of the sound by partially or totally blocking the vestibules leading to the external nose. Excessive nasal resonation (hypernasality) resulting from velar insufficiency of one type or another is probably associated most frequently with cleft palate.

Sinuses (Paranasal Sinuses, Air Sinuses)

The sinus cavities are thought to be developmental accidents formed when the facial bones grow away from the relatively stationary cranium. Usually not present at birth, they are not completely formed until puberty or, in some cases, adulthood. The size and shape of the sinuses vary considerably among individuals. There are four pairs of sinuses: *frontal, ethmoidal, maxillary,* and *sphenoidal* (see Fig. 20).

The two frontal sinuses are located in the frontal bone medial and directly posterior to the superciliary arches which give prominence to the eyebrows. Separated medially by a bony septum, each cavity drains into its corresponding middle meatus. Each cavity can be estimated as having a volume of approximately 20 cubic centimeters; however, because of individual differences this estimate may vary considerably.

The ethmoidal sinuses are numerous (they vary in number from 3 to 18) tiny, thin-walled intercommunicating cavities located in the labyrinth of the ethmoid bone between the orbit of the eye and the nasal cavity, and just below the cranium. They are arranged on each side into three groups, the anterior, middle and posterior ethmoidal sinuses. The anterior and middle ethmoidal cavities open into the middle meatus; the posterior, into the superior meatus. The volume of the cavities on each side is estimated at 7.5 cubic centimeters.

The two maxillary sinuses occupy the hollow portion of each maxillary bone in the cheek area. The largest of the sinuses, each lies lateral to the lower half of the nasal cavity below the orbit and above the molar and premolar teeth. Drainage is offered by an opening in the medial side into the middle meatus. Several additional drainage canals open into the nasal cavity. These, however, are frequently located higher than the sinus floor presenting problems in drainage during nasal congestion. The cilia normally propel the mucous of the mucous membrane toward the openings; however, during inflammation the cilia cannot accommodate the increased quantity of secretion. Each maxillary sinus is estimated as having a volume of 25 cubic centimeters.

The sphenoidal sinus is a large cavity within the sphenoid bone which occupies the central portion of the base of the skull. The cavity is just above and behind the nasal cavities and above and slightly anterior to the nasopharynx. Although the division is incomplete, a central bony septum divides the cavity into two. On each side a duct communicates with the superior meatus of the nasal cavities. The combined volume of the sphenoidal sinuses is estimated at 20 cubic centimeters.

Because of the tiny openings into the various sinus cavities, as well as the comparatively small volume of each, the sinuses cannot logically be considered significant resonators. Perhaps they do contribute in some individuals whose facial structure provides for more than the average sinus volume. However, individuals known to have only chronic sinus congestion with no concomitant nasal cavity inflammation, and who complain of severe pain as a result, rarely reveal any vocal evidence of the condition.

RESONATION AND SPEECH SOUNDS

If while the vowel [*a*] is being produced, the mandible is slightly elevated, the lips protruded and the back of the tongue drawn backward, and the front of the tongue depressed and retracted, the audible sound becomes the [o] vowel. There may be in addition some slight alterations of the pharynx and possibly the laryngeal cavities; however, the important thing to observe is that the sound being generated at the vocal folds remains the same; there is no readjustment of the laryngeal muscles to accommodate for a new position of the folds. The difference between the two vowel phonemes has been caused primarily by changing the size, shape, and exit and entrance from and into the oral cavity. Thus, although we may also correctly speak of *vowel articulation* since articulators—tongue, jaw, lips—are of major importance in vowel production, the sound differences are the result of resonation. All different speech phonemes are auditorily identifiable because their resonation characteristics are different—consonants as well as vowels.

Since the classification of vowels into front, central and back is normally thoroughly discussed in courses in phonetics or speech perception, they will not be listed here. It might be interesting at this point, however, for the student to review the vowel classification paying particular attention to the changing shape, size and apertures of the cavities involved. It might also be interesting to explore the changing characteristics of the [k] phoneme by progressively sliding the dorsum of the tongue forward on the palate while producing it. The resonating characteristics, of course, vary among individuals; however, it is quite easy to perceive what might be described as a back, central and front [k] phone. As many as twelve different alterations of the sound can, reportedly, all be classified as the [k] phoneme.

Exactly what happens in the speech apparatus to produce the various speech phonemes has been one of the primary concerns of speech scientists for many years. Some early investigators believed the sound produced at the vocal folds was composed of a fundamental and a rich supply of overtones. The frequencies did not, however, correspond to the natural frequencies of the resonators; however, the various resonators were set into vibration by the puffs of air produced at the folds and resonated at their own natural frequencies. Thus the tones produced at the folds were unrelated to those produced in the cavities. The two tones, one produced at the folds, and the other by the cavities, combine to create the various vowels. This theory is known as the *cavity-tone* theory.

According to the *harmonic* theory the complex sound produced at the vocal folds is composed of a fundamental and a rich supply of harmonics (exact multiples of the fundamental). Certain of the frequencies produced correspond closely to the natural resonance frequencies of some of the various resonators. Thus, those frequencies which correspond will be reenforced; those not reenforced will be damped. The frequencies reenforced will determine the identity of each phoneme. Unlike the cavity-tone theory, the cavities add no new tones to that originally produced at the folds.

Most speech science laboratories are now equipped to provide considerable objective evidence with which to evaluate concepts relative to resonation. With the harmonic analyzer, for example, it is possible to determine which frequencies are receiving the most energy in any speech phone. This information is plotted on what is called an *acoustic spectrum.*

In plotting the various speech sounds an analysis may show two or three regions of maximal energy; two ordinarily indicates the oral and pharyngeal cavities were involved; three indicates these, plus the nasal cavity. (Audiologists have found such data especially valuable since they frequently need to be able to predict what speech phonemes will probably be affected by a loss of hearing at certain frequencies.)

For the student who is fascinated by the kind of investigations described above, courses in experimental phonetics, advanced linguistics and advanced speech science are normally concerned with these matters.

Resonance, it should be clear at this point, is an extremely important aspect of effective oral speech. Since it is a comparatively subtle aspect of the total speech process, it has probably not received as much attention as some of the other speech variables. However, with the addition of new speech science laboratories in many training centers throughout the country, plus the refinement of equipment, it seems quite likely a great deal more will eventually be known about resonance.

Chapter 9

ARTICULATION

ARTICULATION LITERALLY MEANS "joining together." In the production of oral speech it refers to the shaping of resonators, their apertures, and the texture of their walls, and to the partial or total impedence of the exhaled air stream to produce those sounds which have become identified with speaking the English language.

There are in terms of the definition two aspects to be considered in a study of articulation. They are (1) the speech sounds themselves, and (2) the anatomical structures necessary for producing the sounds, and the muscles related to their movements.

SPEECH SOUNDS

Individual speech sounds are called *phones.* Phones produced with very close acoustic and physiological similarities that are perceived by the speakers of a given language as functionally the same are called *phonemes,* or sound families. For example the [k] phoneme may be produced with numerous, subtle sound differences (phones) all of which, nevertheless, would be classified or identified as a [k] phoneme. Although the total number of phonemes may vary somewhat depending upon the language, there are more than forty in the English language.

The study of speech sounds is sometimes considered the specific province of phoneticians who, using a special alphabet called the International Phonetic Alphabet (IPA) develop great skill in transcribing speech exactly as it is heard. The IPA is of considerable value to speech pathologists for recording speech deviations of various kinds. Occasionally, it is possible only by using the IPA to record exactly how certain speech sounds are being misarticulated.

Linguists are also concerned with speech sounds and sound families. However, their area of specialization, called linguistics, is, among other things, related to finer shades of sound differences than those studied in phonetics. Courses in linguistics are usually related to studies of language structure and language development from an anthropological point of view.

There have been three major approaches to the classification of speech sounds: the *acoustic, placement* and *kinesiological.*

Acoustic

The acoustic classification emphasizes the way a sound is perceived by the auditory mechanism. Four major groups are classified: vowels, semivowels, diphthongs, and consonants. (Consonants are usually defined as voiced or unvoiced sounds requiring either complete or partial obstruction of the air stream for their production. Vowels are voiced sounds, requiring comparatively little or no obstruction of the air stream for their production.)

Consonants are subdivided into voiced sounds (sonants) and unvoiced sounds (surds). The sonants and surds are further subdivided into fricatives and sibilants. Fricatives are consonant sounds produced by forcing air through a narrow opening. Sibilants are very high frequency fricatives produced by forcing air through an opening. Vowels are described as "long," "short," "stressed," "unstressed," etc.

Placement

The placement classification emphasizes the location of the various articulators as the sound is being produced. Terms like "bilabial" (both lips), "labiodental" (lips and teeth) and "velar" (soft palate) are used. The [b] phoneme, for example, would be classified as a bilabial since both lips are closed tightly in order to produce the sound. Vowels are "front," "middle," or "back."

Kinesiological

The kinesiological classification emphasizes the movement necessary to accomplish the various positions required for making the sound. Terms like "stop," "continuant," "glide," and "plosive" are used. Since the [s] sound is produced with a continuous escape of air, it is called a continuant. The [p] sound, however, requiring a total obstruction of the airstream by the lips and a consequent explosion of air as the lips are abruptly released, is called a stop or plosive.

It is quite common for classifications to include terminology of all three categories. Thus the [b] phoneme is often called a voiced, bilabial plosive; the [f], a voiceless, labiodental continuant. Both are consonants.

Since students majoring in speech pathology or audiology will already have had a course in phonetics, no further need for an additional discussion of phonetics is assumed.

ANATOMICAL STRUCTURES RELATED TO ARTICULATION

The mouth, or oral cavity, is the major structure related to articulation. Its associated parts—lips, cheeks, hard and soft palate (velum), tongue, teeth, and jaw—all related to basic biological movements for sucking, biting, and chewing, are all involved in various ways for the production of speech sounds.

Mouth (Oral Cavity)

The mouth or oral cavity can be considered as two cavities: the *outer cavity* or *vestibule* (buccal cavity), and the *inner cavity.* The outer cavity is bounded by the lips and cheeks externally and the closed teeth and gums internally. The inner cavity is bounded on the front and sides by the gums and teeth. The roof of the cavity is formed by the hard and soft palate. (The *maxillae,* each maxilla consisting of a body and four processes, unite to form what is usually called the upper jaw. The processes are alveolar, frontal, palatine, and zygomatic. The palatine process forms most of the roof of the mouth and the floor of the nose.) The floor of the inner cavity contains mucous membrane, a large portion of the tongue, the mylohyoid and geniohyoid muscles.

The outer cavity contains many glands—labial glands on the inner surface of the lip, and molar glands opening from the cheeks opposite the back teeth. Stenson's ducts of the parotid salivary glands open opposite the second upper molars.

Lips

The lips are muscular, fleshy folds containing blood vessels, labial glands, and connective tissue composed of elastic and inelastic fibers meshing into a network. The lips are covered externally by skin and internally by mucous membrane. There are glands directly underneath the mucous membrane.

The skin of the lips ends in a sharp line called the vermillion line where a transitional zone, the vermilion zone, lies between the skin and the mucous membrane. The vermilion epithelium covering this area is thin, and the cells contain eleiden which increases their transparency so that the underlying capillaries appear red.

The *labial frenulum,* a vertical fold of mucous membrane on the inside of the upper lip, connects the lip to the alveolar process of the maxillae. A similar, but weaker, frenulum is located in the inner portion of the lower lip.

In addition to the primitive function of suckling, the lips, sensitive to touch and temperature, reject unsuitable material for the mouth. They also assist in transporting food and liquid into the mouth and in preventing their escape during mastication.

Cheeks (Buccae)

The fleshy mass forming the lateral portion of the face is composed chiefly of the buccinator muscle as well as platysma, risorius and zygomaticus muscles. The cheeks are covered externally by skin and internally by mucous membrane which fuses above and below with the gums and behind with the mucosa of the soft palate.

The lateral walls of the oral cavity are continuous with the lateral walls of the pharynx via the buccinator muscle which attaches to the superior constrictor of the pharynx.

Although not nearly so important as the lips, the cheeks assist in the total process of mastication and in the retention of food.

Muscles of the Lips and Cheeks (Muscles of Expression)

The muscles which follow are used primarily for biological purposes as the lips engage in sucking, chewing, repelling foreign matter, etc. Their relationship to expressing feelings and attitudes and to producing and resonating speech sounds has come about as the result of man's need to communicate.

Orbicularis Oris (Unpaired). This muscle is located entirely within the lips and completely encircles the opening into the mouth. (It is not clear whether orbicularis oris is a distinct entity, partly a separate muscle and partly fibers from other muscles, or merely the continuation of the fibers of other muscles. However, since numerous muscles in this group insert into the lips, it seems logical to suspect that it is probably formed from other muscles.) Its action is primarily to close the lips. It can also narrow them, protrude and pucker them, and draw the lower lip down and the upper lip up. This muscle, as well as all the others in this group, is innervated by C-VII. Sensory innervation comes from C-V. Figure 21 shows all the muscles listed.

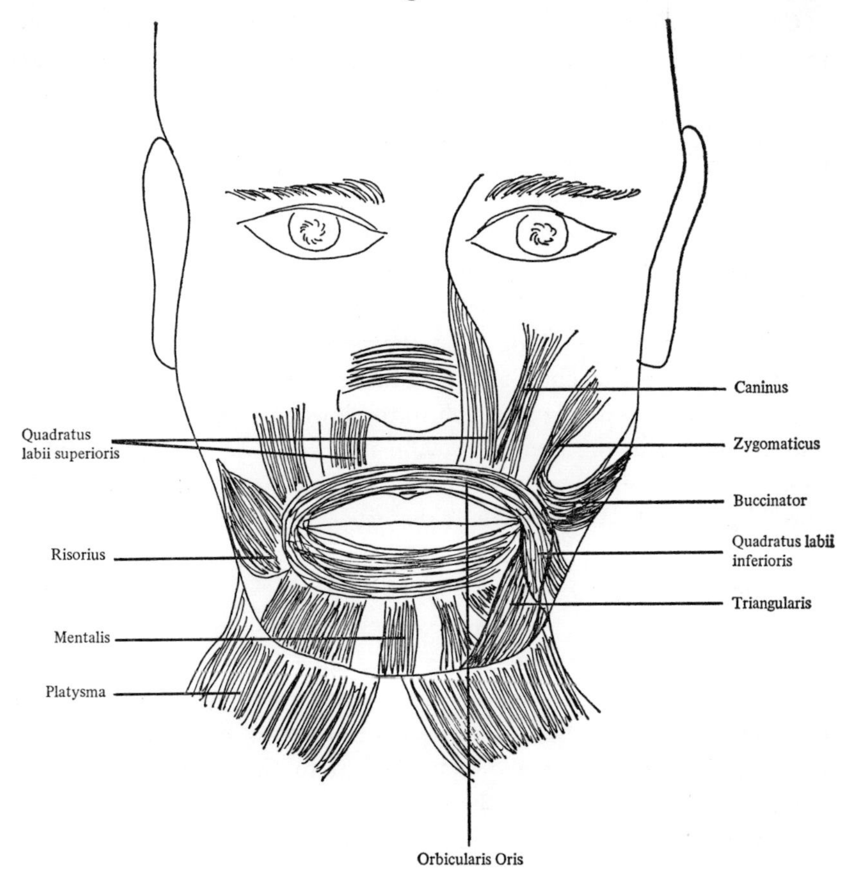

FIGURE 21. Muscles of the lips and cheeks. (Muscles of expression.)

Quadratus Labii Superioris (Paired). This flat, triangular muscle is located above the lateral portion of the upper lip. Fibers from its three heads (angular, infraorbital, zygomatic) converge and insert near the angle of the mouth. The common action is to raise the upper lip, elevate the corner of the mouth and wing of the nose.

Quadratus Labii Inferioris (Paired). Flat and quadrangular, this muscle is located below the lateral portion of the mouth. Attaches from the outer surface of the mandible below the angle of the mouth into orbicularis oris and the skin of the lower lip; some few fibers insert into the skin of the chin. Its action draws the lower lip downward and slightly lateralward producing an expression of irony.

Caninus (Paired). This is a flat, triangular muscle located above the corner of the mouth. Deep to quadratus labii superioris, it attached below the infraorbital foramen, descends downward and slightly laterally to the corner of the mouth where some fibers insert; others end in the skin and mucous membrane of the lower lip. Its action elevates the corner of the mouth and helps to close the mouth by elevating the lower lip. Produces the expression of sneering.

Platysma (Paired). This wide, quadrilateral muscle covers most of the anterior and lateral surface of the neck. It extends from the chest to the face. Attaching from the skin and superficial connective tissue in the superior chest and deltoid regions, it travels upward and forward. Some of its fibers attach to the lower border of the mandible and connect with the quadratus labii inferioris and triangularis muscles. Additional fibers extending up into the face at the level of the lower lip cross to the opposite side. Its action draws the angles of the mouth down and laterally producing an expression of distain.

Risorius (Paired). This is a flat muscle lateral to the mouth and superficial to the platysma. Highly variable, it is sometimes entirely missing. It attaches to the connective tissue over the masseter muscle (discussed later) and crosses horizontally to the corner of the mouth. Most of the fibers insert into the skin and mucosa of the upper lip and the mucosa directly lateral to the mouth. Some few fibers terminate in the lower lip. Its action retracts the corner of the mouth producing an expression of grinning, threatening or sneering.

Buccinator (Paired). This is the major muscle of the cheeks. It attaches from the molar area of the upper and lower alveoli, from the pterygomandibular raphe (a tendinous structure between the buccinator and superior pharyngeal constrictor giving origin to the middle parts of both muscles) and from the outer alveolar border of the mandible in the molar area. Its fibers extend into both the upper and lower lips and interlace with those of the opposite side. Its action pulls the angle of the mouth laterally and posteriorly; keeps the cheeks stretched during any oral activity, narrows the mouth and enables the lips and cheeks to be pressed against the teeth.

Triangularis (Paired). This is a flat, triangular muscle located superficial and slightly lateral to quadratus labii inferioris. Attaches from the oblique angle of the outer surface of the mandible. Alternating with fibers from the platysma, both converge as they ascend to the corner of the mouth where they insert partly into the skin of the mouth angle and the upper lip. Its action pulls the mouth angle down. When both sides act simultaneously, the mouth is closed because of the depression of the upper lip producing an expression of contempt.

Mentalis (Paired). This muscle lies close to the midline of the mouth and below it. Attaches from the fossa of the mandible close to the level of the lower lip. Its fibers descend to insert into the skin of the chin. Its action raises and wrinkles the skin of the chin and protrudes the lower lip and turns it outward. The expression associated with doubt or distain is created by action of mentalis.

Zygomaticus (Paired). This flat, oblong muscle attaches from the temporal process of the zygomatic bone, travels downward and medially to insert into orbicularis oris and the skin of the angle of the mouth. Its action pulls the corners of the mouth upward and laterally, producing the expression of laughing.

Although it could be argued that every muscle listed above is not actually used by all in the production of speech sounds, the majority are. There is considerable individual difference in the production of certain phonemes. All of the bilabials and the labiodentals normally require use of the lips for their production. The remaining consonants as well as the vowels require variable adjustments of the lips and surrounding area for their production.

Some, it should be noted, produce phonemes in what might be called an unorthodox manner. The [f] phoneme, for example, normally produced by pressing the upper teeth over the lower lip and emitting a continuous stream of air, is produced by some by merely pressing the upper teeth behind the lower lip which is slightly protruded as the air is emitted.

The Teeth

A tooth consists of an exposed portion protruding from the gums called the *crown,* a portion embedded in the socket (alveolus) of the jaw bone called the *root,* and a portion connecting the crown and the root called the *neck.*

Each tooth has a solid outer portion and a central pulp cavity. The outer portion consists of an ivory substance, dentine, forming the main body of the tooth, and a very hard substance, enamel, covering the crown. The enamel is the hardest substance in the body. The root of the tooth is covered by a thin layer of hard material, substantia ossea, or cement. The tooth socket is lined with periosteum which supplies nourishment and attaches the tooth to the socket. The pulp cavity extends lengthwise through the center of the tooth; blood vessels and nerves enter it through openings in the root tip.

The child has a temporary, or deciduous, set of twenty teeth which are gradually replaced from about six years of age by the thirty-two permanent teeth. The first set of teeth normally has erupted by the second year of life. The permanent teeth originate with the first molars which erupt just behind the last deciduous teeth. The permanent teeth are essentially established about the twelfth year.

The approximate ages for the eruption of the teeth are as follows:

DECIDUOUS TEETH

Kind of Teeth	*Months*
Lower central incisors	6-9
Upper incisors	8-10
Lateral incisors and first molars	15-21
Canines (cuspids)	16-20
Second molars	20-24

PERMANENT TEETH

Kind of Teeth	*Years*
First molars	6
Central incisors	7
Lateral incisors	8
First premolars (bicuspids)	9
Second premolars	10
Canines (cuspids)	11-12
Second molars	12-13
Third molars (wisdom)	17-25

The permanent set of teeth finally appearing in one jaw include four incisors (two central and two lateral), two canine (cuspids), four premolars (bicuspids), and six molars.

Occlusion. When the jaws are approximated the upper and lower teeth have a relationship to each other called *occlusion.* In normal occlusion the upper teeth (incisors and canines) overlap the lowers approximately one third. Normally there is no overlapping of the molars.

Malocclusion. This refers to failure of the dental arches to occlude properly. Angle (1907) has classified malocclusions as follows:

Class I (Neutroclusion). Normal mesiodistal relation of the dental arches with contracted and undeveloped maxillary arches especially in the anterior portion in which teeth often assume varied forms of individual malocclusion.

Class II (Distoclusion). The lower dental arch is distal to the upper on one or both lateral halves.

Division 1. Bilaterally distal with protruding upper incisors.

Division 2. Bilaterally distal with retruding upper incisors.

Subdivision. Unilaterally distal with retruding upper incisors.

Class III (Mesioclusion). The lower dental arch is mesial to the upper on one or both lateral halves with protruding lower incisors.

Subdivision. Unilaterally mesial with protruding lower incisors.

Class IV (Cross Bite). The occlusion relations of the dental arches present the unusual condition of being in distal occlusion upon one lateral half, and in mesial occlusion upon the other half.

A *close-bite* refers to an occlusion in which the labial teeth pass their proper occlusial planes so that the lower incisors strike the gum behind the upper incisors. An *open-bite* refers to an occlusion in which the labial teeth are prevented from coming together when the buccal teeth are occluded.

All of the teeth may be absent in an adult with no noticcable effect on speech. And the fact that a skilled ventriloquist is able to produce all speech sounds with no noticeable movement of the articulators suggests that speech sounds can be produced using neither the teeth nor the lips. However, as speech is being learned, absence of teeth or a malocclusion may interfere seriously with the production of various sounds.

Mandible

The mandible, or lower jaw, is the largest and strongest of the facial bones. Biologically the mandible supports the teeth, and by its movements is a major factor in mastication.

The mandible consists of a central, horizontal portion, the *body,* or *corpus,* which is roughly U-shaped, forming the chin and supporting the teeth; and two perpendicular portions, the *rami,* projecting upward from the back of the body on either side. On the upper border of the body is the alveolar process into which the teeth insert. Just below the first bicuspid, about halfway between the upper and lower margins of the jaw, is the *mental foramen* (see Fig. 22).

Each ramus has a condyle for articulation with the temporal bone at the temporomandibular joint, and a coronoid process for attach-

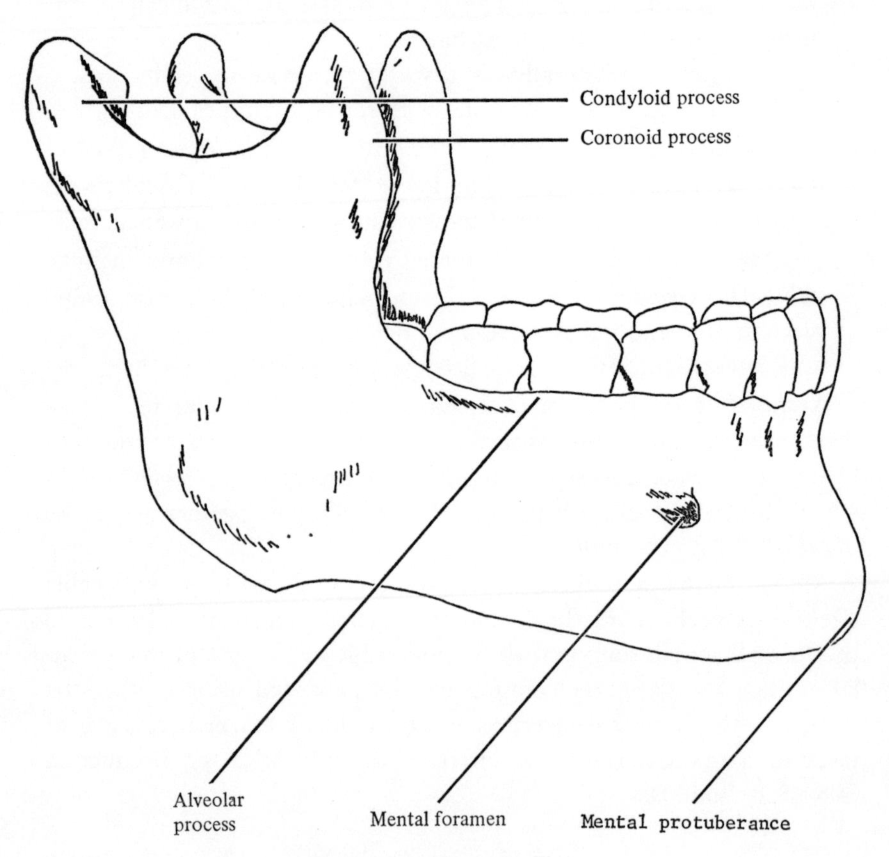

FIGURE 22. The mandible.

ment of the temporalis muscle. On the medial surface of the ramus is an opening, the mandibular foramen, through which pass the vessels and nerves for the teeth. At the base of the mandible where the body joins the ramus is a groove for the external maxillary artery. The *mandibular symphasis* is the midpoint of the chin marking the junction between the two halves of the mandible. The projected tip is the *mental protuberance.*

There are two lines associated with the mandible; the *oblique line* which is a slight ridge running obliquely externally from a low point anteriorly to a high point posteriorly, and the *mylohyoid line* running internally upward and posteriorly toward the ramus.

Muscles Associated with Movements of the Mandible

The chief movements of the mandible are elevation and depression. However the mandible may also be protruded and slightly retracted. The following muscles are related to these movements.

Masseter (Paired). This muscle is the most superficial of the group. It stretches as a thick, flat mass over the outer surface of the mandibular ramus. It has two parts, superficial and deep; both originate on the zygomatic arch and insert upon the ramus or the angle of the mandible. Its action strongly elevates the lower jaw and supplies pressure on the molars. The deep portion can also retract; the superficial portion, protrude. This muscle, as well as all the others in this group, is innervated by the mandibular branch of C-V (see Fig. 23).

Temporalis (Paired). This is a triangular sheet-like muscle attaching from a large area on the side of the skull called the temporal fossa. It extends deep to the zygomatic arch and converges toward the coronoid process of the mandible where it extends as far down as a ramus of the jaw. Its action elevates primarily; however, some of the fibers possess a retracting function.

Internal Pterygoid (Paired). A thick, quadrilateral muscle roughly paralleling the masseter, but lying on the medial surface of the mandibular ramus, this muscle is somewhat weaker than masseter. It attaches from the pterygoid fossa of the sphenoid bone with some fibers also attaching from the lateral pterygoid plate. The

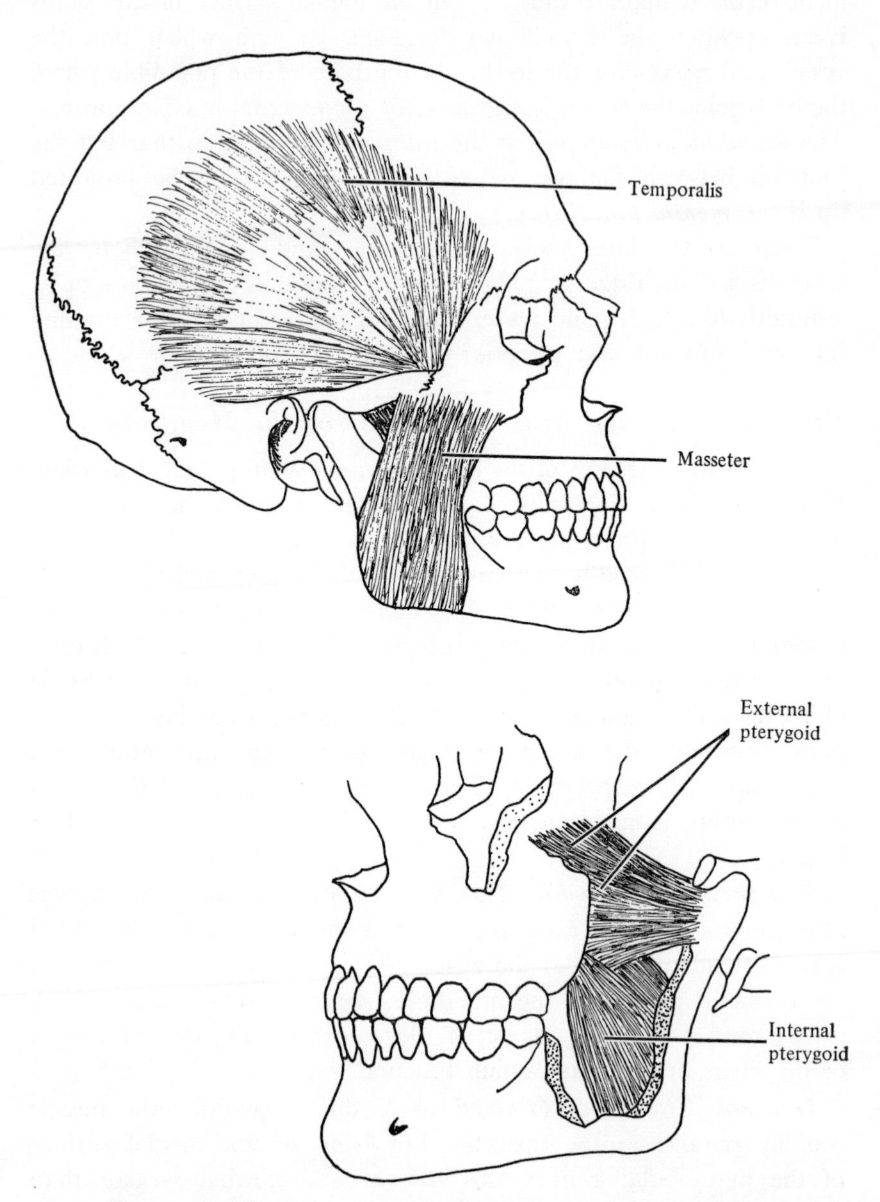

FIGURE 23. Muscles associated with movements of the mandible.

fibers extend downward, backward and slightly outward to the medial surface of the mandible near its angle. Its action elevates the mandible, protrudes it and pulls it laterally.

External Pterygoid (Paired). This muscle is thick and triangular and is located deep to temporalis. It attaches from two heads—the larger inferior head from the lateral pterygoid plate and the smaller superior head from the infratemporal surface of the greater wing of the sphenoid bone. The two fuse as they pass in front of the temporomandibular joint. The fibers travel backward and outward to the condyloid process of the mandible and the capsule of the temporomandibular joint. Its action protrudes the mandible. When acting unilaterally, it draws the mandible outward.

In addition to the muscles listed, several of the suprahyoid group—mylohyoid, genihyoid and the anterior belly of diagastric—are associated with mandibular movement. The former two retract the mandible, the latter depresses it.

In producing speech sounds, all the vowels require a depression of the mandible for their production; all of the consonants, with the exception of [m], [n] and [ŋ], require either some depression, elevation or retraction of the mandible to be produced without distortion. The mandible must be considered an important factor in articulating and resonating speech sounds.

Tongue

The tongue (lingua) is located on the floor of the mouth. Its root, directed backward, has four attachments: to the soft palate by the glossopalatine faucial pillars; to the pharynx by the superior constrictor; to the hyoid bone by the hyoglossal muscles; and to the epiglottis by the glossoepiglottic folds.

Its tip (lingual apex) is normally directed forward against the inner surface of the lower incisors. The upper surface (dorsum) is convex and marked into halves by the median sulcus. Its anterior two-thirds is covered by the papillae including the taste buds. The posterior portion of the tongue dips downward in front of the pharynx almost to the level of the hyoid bone and overhangs the epiglottis. The under surface of the tongue is connected by the genioglossi to the mandible. The *lingual frenulum* is a fold of mucous membrane which connects the under surface of the tongue to the floor of the mouth. When the mouth is closed, the tongue contacts the palate and almost fills the oral cavity.

Biologically the tongue has an important role in mastication. It transfers food to various areas of the mouth and helps mix the particles with saliva. It transports food ready for swallowing from the teeth to the rear portion of the mouth, and presses food against the hard palate to facilitate crushing. The tongue also acts as a kind of sweeper removing bits of food from the mouth after swallowing. The taste and general sensory receptors of the dorsum are important in regulating the temperature and kind of food intake.

Muscles Related to Activity of the Tongue

There are two groups of muscles related to the movements of the tongue: the *extrinsic* muscles having their origin outside the tongue; and the *intrinsic* muscles contained entirely within the tongue. The former effect the changes of position of the tongue mass and tongue form; the latter influence only the form of the tongue.

The Extrinsics. *Genioglossus (paired)* attaches from the mental spine of the mandible. Its fibers travel horizontally to the base of the tongue and insert into the body of the hyoid bone. Most of the fibers radiate to the dorsum extending from tip to base. The action of the various fibers of this muscle protrude and elevate the tongue, move the tip back and down, and depress the median portion to form a concavity to accept food. All of the muscles in this as well as the intrinsic group are innervated by C-XII (see Fig. 24).

Styloglossus (paired)—this elongated muscle extends from the styloid process of the temporal bone to the apex of the tongue. Its action retracts and elevates the entire tongue.

Hyoglossus (paired)—this quadrilateral sheet of fibers extends from the hyoid bone to the side of the tongue. Its fibers interlace with the horizontal fibers of styloglossur. Its action draws the tongue downward and backward.

Glossopalatinus (paired)—this muscle has been described previously in connection with the veolpharyngeal closure. Its action is to elevate the posterior portion of the tongue.

The Intrinsics. *Superior longitudinal (unpaired)*—this muscle

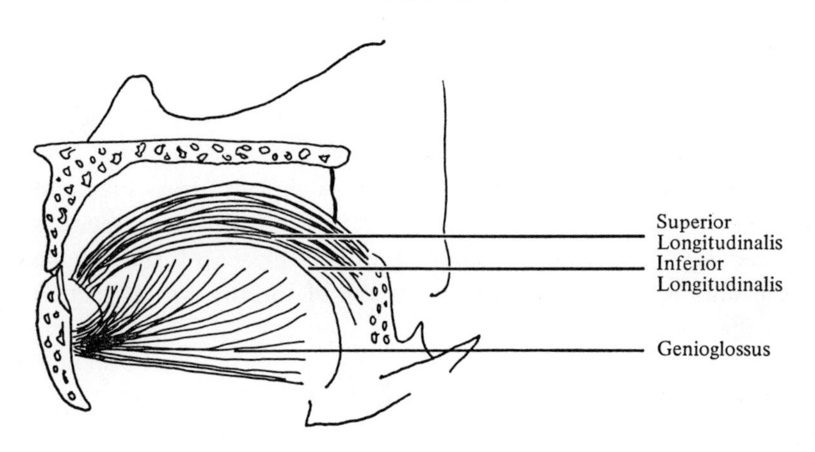

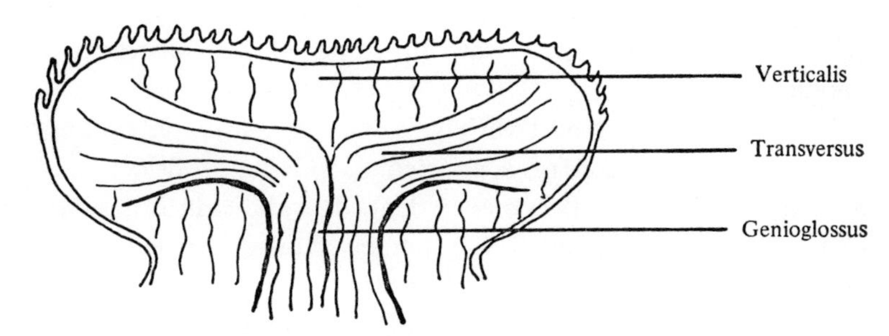

FIGURE 24. Muscles of the tongue.

lies directly beneath the mucous membrane and extends along the dorsum from the root to the tip. Its fibers insert into the skin along the borders and tip. Its action bulges the tongue upward in a longitudinal direction, and it can retract and curl the lingual apex (see Fig. 24).

Inferior longitudinal (paired)—this rounded muscle attaches from the hyoid bone and undersurface of the tongue, and its fibers extending downward and forward insert into the tip of the tongue. Its action shortens the tip from front to back. It can also depress the tip.

Transversus (paired)—this muscle forms much of the fleshy portion of the tongue. Its horizontal layers fan out as they travel laterally toward the dorsum and lateral margins. Does not reach either the dorsal surface or the tongue tip. Its action narrows the tongue and thus protrudes it; it may also bulge the tongue upward; and its lateral fibers can elevate the sides to form a groove.

Verticalis (paired)—with transversus, this muscle forms much of the flesh of the tongue. The vertical fibers, whose actual presence is questioned by some, extend from the upper surface of the tongue near the sides and tip to the under surface of the tongue. Its action flattens the tongue.

Action of the Tongue in Speech Production

The tongue is considered by many to be the primary and most important organ of articulation and resonation. Working in conjunction with the mandible it modifies the shape and size and entrance and exit of the oral cavity. The production of vowels is especially related to tongue movement in dividing the oral cavity. The majority of the consonants require the impeding of the airstream via the tongue.

When the number and variety of movements made by the tongue during the production of connected speech are considered, the significance of this organ becomes evident. It is difficult, if not impossible, to think of the activity of the tongue during connected speech as isolated muscle movements. It appears, rather, that much of speech sound production becomes functionally autonomous, and if one accepts such an argument, it should logically follow that oral reading and spontaneous conversational speech very often expected of all elementary grade children should not be anticipated until all speech phonemes have been mastered and the tongue, mandible and lips are operating autonomously enough to permit the child to concentrate on other aspects of communication.

Speculation in this area is, however, far easier than the accumulation of supporting data with which to formulate a theory. The extensive processes involved in speech sound production—which should be quite clear to the student at this point—are enormously complicated, and some are impossible to objectify. However, considering the large number of individuals with articulation defects, more attention probably needs to be given to this phase of oral communication than it has received in the past.

REFERENCES

1. ANGLE, E. H.: *Malocclusion of the Teeth,* 7th ed. Philadelphia, S. S. White Dental Mfg. Co., 1907.
2. BASMAJIAN, J. V.: *Primary Anatomy,* 5th ed. Baltimore, Williams & Wilkins, 1964.
3. BLOOMER, H. H.: A roentgenographic study of the mechanics of respiration. *Speech Monogr, 3*:118, 1936.
4. BLOOMER, H. H.: Observation on palatopharyngeal movements in speech and deglutition. *J Speech Hearing Dis, 10*:2,230, 1953.
5. BROCA, P.: Remarques sur le siege de la faculté du language articulé, suivi d'une observation d'aphemie. *Bull Soc Anat, 6*:330, 1861.
6. BROCA, P.: *Memoirs Sur Le Cerreau de l'Homme.* Paris, Reinwald, 1888.
7. BRODNITZ, F.: *Vocal Rehabilitation.* Rochester, Minn., Whiting Press, 1959.
8. CUNNINGHAM, D.: *Textbook of Anatomy,* 9th ed. Edited by J. C. Brash. New York, Oxford U. P., 1951.
9. DELACATO, C. H.: *The Diagnosis and Treatment of Speech and Reading Problems.* Springfield, Ill., Thomas, 1963.
10. DIEHL, C. F., AND COHEN, J. H.: Relation of speech-sound discrimination ability to articulation type speech defects. *J Speech Hearing Dis, 28*:2,187, 1963.
11. DIEHL, C. F.; WHITE, R., AND BURK, K. W.: Voice quality and anxiety. *J Speech Hearing Res, 2*:2,282, 1959.
12. DOLLARD, J., AND MILLER, N. E.: *Personality and Psychotherapy.* New York, McGraw-Hill, 1950.
13. DORLAND, W. A.: *Dorland's Illustrated Medical Dictionary,* 23rd ed. Philadelphia, Saunders, 1951.
14. DRAPER, M. H.; LADEFOGED, P., AND WHITTERIDGE, D.: Respiratory muscles in speech. *J Speech Hearing Res, 2*:1,16, 1959.
15. EDWARDS, A.: *Vocabulary Guide to Neuroanatomy.* Berkeley, Calif., East Bay Publishing Co., 1967.
16. FAABORG-ANDERSON, K.: *Electromyography of Laryngeal Muscles in Humans. Techniques and Results,* Vol. 3. Basel, S. Karger, 1965.
17. GARDNER, E.: *Fundamentals of Neurology.* Philadelphia, Saunders, 1963.
18. GRAY, H.: *Anatomy of the Human Body,* 33rd ed. Edited by C. M. Goss. Philadelphia, Lea and F., 1954.
19. HEBB, D. O.: *The Organization of Behavior.* New York, Wiley, 1949.
20. HELTMAN, H. J.: Contradictory evidence in handedness and stuttering. *J Speech Hearing Dis, 5*:3,327, 1940.
21. HILLIER, W. F., JR.: Total left cerebral hemispherectomy for malignant glioma. *Neurology, 4*:718, 1954.

22. Hoshiko, M. S.: Sequence of action of breathing muscles during speech. *J Speech Hearing Dis, 3*:3,291, 1960.

23. Husson, R.: Etude des phénomenes physiologiques et acoustiques fondamentaux de la voix cantée. *Disp edit Rev scientifique,* 1-91, 1950.

24. Judson, L. S. V., and Weaver, A. T.: *Voice Science,* 2nd ed. New York, Appleton, 1965.

25. Kann, J.: A translation of Broca's original article on the location of the speech center. *J Speech Hearing Dis, 15*:16, 1950.

26. Kaplan, H. M.: *Anatomy and Physiology of Speech.* New York, McGraw-Hill, 1960.

27. Kephart, N.: *The Slow Learner in the Classroom.* Columbus, Ohio, C. E. Merrill, 1960.

28. Kimura, D.: Left-right differences in the perception of melodies. *Quart J Exp Psychol, 16*:355, 1964.

29. Kimura, D.: Speech lateralization in young children as determined by an auditory test. *J Comp Physiol Psychol, 56*:5,899, 1963.

30. Kimura, D.: Some effects of temporal-lobe damage on auditory perception. *Canad J Psychol, 15*:5,156, 1961.

31. Kimura, D.: Cerebral dominance and the perception of verbal stimuli. *Canad J Psychol, 15*:3,166, 1961.

32. Kronvall, E. L., and Diehl, C. F.: The relationship of auditory discrimination to articulatory defects of children with no known organic impairment. *J Speech Hearing Dis, 18*:3,335, 1954.

33. Krynauw, H.: Infantile hemiplegia treated by removing one cerebral hemisphere. *J Neurol Psychiat, 13*:243, 1950.

34. Meader, C. L., and Muyskens, J. H.: *Handbook of Biolinguistics.* Part-one-Section A. Toledo, Ohio, Herbert C. Weller, 1950.

35. Millard, N. D.; King, B., and Showers, M. J.: *Human Anatomy and Physiology,* 4th ed. Philadelphia, Saunders, 1956.

36. Moses, P. J.: *The Voice of Neurosis.* New York, Grune and Stratton, 1954.

37. Netter, F. H.: *The Ciba Collection of Medical Illustrations. Vol. I: Nervous System.* Summit, N. J., CIBA Pharmaceutical Products Inc, 1953.

38. Peele, T. L.: *The Neuroanatomical Basis for Clinical Neurology.* New York, McGraw-Hill, 1954.

39. Penfield, W., and Roberts, L.: *Speech and Brain Mechanisms.* Princeton, N.J., Princeton, U. P., 1959.

40. Pressman, J. J., and Kelemen, G.: Physiology of the larynx. *Physiol Rev, 35*:3,506, 1955.

41. Saunders, W. H.: The Larynx. In *Clinical Symposia,* 16.3.67. Summit, N.J., Ciba Pharmaceutical Co, 1964.

42. Shankweiler, D.: Effects of temporal-lobe damage on perception of dichotically presented melodies. *J Comp Physiol Psychol, 62*:1,115, 1966.

43. SHEARER, W. M.: *Illustrated Speech Anatomy.* Springfield, Ill., Thomas, 1963.
44. VAN DEN BERG, J.: Myoelastic-aerodynamic theory of voice production. *J Speech Hearing Res, 1*:3,227-244, 1958.
45. WERNICKE, C.: *Der Aphasische Symptomencomplex.* Breslaw, Cohen and Weigert, 1874.
46. WEVER, G.: *Theory of Hearing.* New York, Wiley, 1949.
47. WEST, R.: The neurophysiology of speech. In Travis, L. E., (Ed.): *Handbook of Speech Pathology.* New York, Appleton, 1957.
48. WEST, R.; ANSBERRY, M., AND CARR, A.: *The Rehabilitation of Speech,* 3rd ed. New York, Harpers, 1957.
49. WOODBURNE, L. S.: *The Neural Basis of Behavior.* Columbus, Ohio, C. E. Merrill, 1967.

GLOSSARY

Abduction (ab-DUCK-shun).
To draw away from the midline.

Abducens (ab-DU-senz).
The sixth cranial nerve.

Acoustic Spectrum. The distribution of the intensity levels of the various frequency components of a tone complex.

Acromegaly (AK-row-MEG-ahle).
Enlargement of body parts caused by hyperfunction of the anterior pituitary.

Action Potential. Used to describe the electrical disturbance in a nerve fiber during the transmission along it.

Adenoid (AD-uh-noid).
A mass of lymphoid tissue located in about the center of the posterior wall of the nasopharynx; the pharyngeal tonsil, but commonly called adenoids.

Adduction (ad-DUCK-shun).
To draw toward the midline.

Adrenergic (ad-re-NER-jik).
Term applied to those nerves liberating sympathin.

Alveolus (al-VEE-o-lus).
A sac or socket related to the teeth, lungs or glands.

Anomaly (a-NOM-a-ly).
Any deviation from the usual.

Antagonist. An organ, gland, muscle, nerve center so connected physiologically with another the two organs function reciprocally, the action of each tending to counteract the other.

Aperiodic (A-pier-i-AH-dick).
Of irregular occurrence.

Apex. The topmost part of a structure conical or pyramidal in shape.

Aphasia (ah-FAY-ze-ah).
Impairment of the ability to perceive or express symbols.

Aponeurosis (apo-new-ROW-sis).
A tendenous broad band of tissue; usually flat, broad and sheet-like.

Appendicular. Pertaining to an appendage.

Arachnoid Mater (uh-RACK-noyd-may-ter).
A delicate membrane passing over from one cerebral gyrus to another, not dipping down into the sulci like the pia mater.

Ataxia (ah-TACK-see-ah).
Absence or loss of muscular coordination.

Articulation. Literally, a state of being united by a joint or joints. In speech, it refers to the shaping of resonators, their apertures, and the texture of their walls, and to the partial or total impedence of the exhaled air stream to produce the sounds which have become identified with speaking the English language.

Aryepiglottic Folds (air-e-ep-i-GLOT-tic). Bilateral folds of tissue forming the margins of the epiglottis at the opening into the larynx.

Aryepiglottic Muscle. An extension of the oblique arytenoideus muscle. Assists in making the aryepiglottic sphincter closing the laryngeal cavity during swollowing.

Arytenoid (air-e-TEE-noid). Shaped like a pitcher; one of a pair of cartilages mounted on the cricoid cartilage and to which the vocal ligament attaches at the vocal process. The movement of the arytenoids relate to the opening and closing of the vocal folds.

Aryvocalis (air-e-vo-CAL-is). Deep fibers of the vocalis muscle.

Atlas (AT-las). Term for first cervical vertebra.

Axial (AK-see-l). A vertical reference point.

Axis. Term used for second cervical vertebra.

Axon (AK-sun). The conducting part of a nerve fiber.

Basal Ganglia. A compact group of organs of CNS situated below the cortex in midcranial region consisting principally of the striate bodies: basal nuclei.

Bicuspid. Teeth with two prominent cusps or heads.

Bifurcate (BY-fur-kate). Divide into two.

Brachial (BRAY-key-ull). Usually applied to structures and tissues of the arm.

Brain Stem. A term used to describe the midbrain, pons and medulla which have many structures and functions in common; in it are nuclei of motor cranial nerves.

Bronchiole (BRONG-kee-ole). The name applied to each of the divisions resulting from the forking of the trachea into bronchi.

Bronchus (BRONG-kus). Either of the two main branches of the trachea leading into the lungs.

Buccinator Muscle (BUCK-si-nay-tor). Refer to index.

Bulbar. Pertaining to the medulla oblongata.

Bursa (BUR-sah). A sac or sac-like cavity filled with a sticky fluid and situated at places in the tissue at which friction would otherwise develop.

Canine (KAY-nine). Name for long, pointed teeth.

Calamus Scriptorius (KAL-a-mus scrip-TOR-i-us).

Space at lower part or floor of the fourth ventricle, between restiform bodies where respiratory centers are located.

Caninus Muscles (kay-NEYE-nus). Refer to index.

Capsule (CAP-sule). An enveloping structure; a capsular ligament (of a joint).

Carotid (kah-ROT-id). Arteries running to the brain; to head.

Cartilage (KAHR-ti-lidj). A type of body tissue intermediary between bone and epithelium, furnishing strength, shape, and flexibility.

Cauda Equina (CAW-da eek-WHY-na). Thus called because it looks like a horse's tail; composed of the roots of the lumbar, sacral and coccygeal nerves as they run a long way down within the spinal canal in this formation before exiting.

Caudate (KAW-date). Possessing a tail.

Caudate Nucleus. A large comma-shaped mass of grey matter located in the forebrain; "nucleus" here means a group of nerve cells with a common function.

Celiac (SEE-lay-ak). Pertaining to the abdomen.

Cerebellum (SAIR-e-BEL-um). Largest part of hindbrain; composed of the vermis, a small central part, and two cerebellar hemispheres. Has grey matter on outside and white matter inside; attached to rest of CNS on each side by three bands of fibers called the superior, middle and inferior cerebellar peduncles.

Cerebral Peduncles (pe-DUNG-kell). Two located in midbrain; prominent bars of tissue containing nerve fibers passing from brain to spinal cord and in opposite direction.

Cerebrospinal Fluid. Clear, colorless fluid filling the ventricles of the brain and the subarachnoid space; its chemical composition is very similar to blood plasma; circulates through ventricles and subarachnoid space inside and outside the brain and cord; eventually absorbed into the blood passing along the venous sinuses; its main function is to protect brain and cord by forming a liquid cushion around them; it also enables pressure within the skull to be kept constant by reacting to any change by an alteration in amount secreted; specimens of fluid may be obtained by lumbar puncture.

Cerebrum (SAIR-e-brum). The two hemispheres forming the main part of the brain, occupying the upper and fore part of cranium.

Choana Narium (ko-AY-nah NA-ri-um). Posterior opening of nares.

Cholinergic (ko-lin-ER-jik). Term applied to those nerves liberating acetylcholine.

Choroid Plexuses (Ko-roid). Vascular fringe-like fold of the pia mater in the third, fourth, and lateral ventricles. Secrete the cerebrospinal fluid.

Clavicle (CLA-vi-kul). A bone of the shoulder girdle articulating medially with the sternum and laterally with the acromion of the scapula: the collarbone.

Coccygeus Muscle (cock-SIDJ-ee-us). Refer to index.

Columella (col-u-MEL-la). The medial, cartilaginous, movable pillar separting the nares.

Collagenous (ko-LAJ-gen-us). Usually white tissue which has a high concentration of the protein collagen; also, usually applied to the white, fibrous connective tissue.

Commissural (ko-MIS-u-ral). Pertaining to or acting as a commisure.

Commisure (KOM-i-sur). Any bundle of nerve fibers connecting corresponding opposite parts.

Concha (KONG-kah). A structure resembling the shape of a shell. Nasal conchae form meatuses of the internal nasal cavity.

Conjunctiva (kon-junk-TIGH-vah). The delicate membrane lining the eyelids and covering the eyeball.

Coronoid (COR-o-noid). Hooked or curved; as the coronoid process of the mandible.

Corniculate (kor-NICK-you-let). A small cartilaginous nodule at the apex of each arytenoid cartilage in the larynx.

Cornu (KORE-new). Horn-shaped structure.

Conus Elasticus (KO-nus e-LAS-ti-cus).

or

Cricovocal Membrane (CRY-ko-VO-cal). The lateral section of the cricothyroid membrane, whose free medial borders form the vocal ligament or platform supporting the vocal folds.

Corpora Quadrigemina (kor-POR-ah quad-rah-GEM-mina). Four small prominences at the back of midbrain; the upper pair (superior colliculi) are concerned with sight reflexes and the lower pair (inferior colliculi) with hearing reflexes.

Corpus (KOR-pus). Any body.

Corpus Callosum (KOR-pus kahl-LOW-sum). A broad, thick band of nerve fibers connecting the two cerebral hemispheres.

Corpus Striatum (KOR-pus streye-ATE-tum). Subcortical mass of grey and white matter anterior to the thalamus in each hemisphere.

Cortex (KOR-tex). Outer layer; outer layer of the brain (cerebral cortex).

Craniotomy (kra-knee-AH-toe-mee). Incision of the skull.

Cricoarytenoid Muscle (CRY-co-air-e-TE-noid). An intrinsic muscle of the larynx. Refer to index.

Cricoid (CRY-koid). Signet shaped; cricoid cartilage of the larynx.

Cutaneous (cue-TAY-knee-us). Pertaining to the first layer of skin.

Cytology (sigh-TAHL-o-gee). Scientific study of cells.

Decussate (deh-CUSS-ate). A crossing action resulting in an X formation; usually applied to nerve groups of the CNS.

Deltoid Muscle (DEL-toid). A large thick delta shaped muscle covering the shoulder joint.

Dendrite (DEN-dright). Short, freely branching processes through which nervous impulses enter the nerve cell.

Dentine (DEN-teen). The calcified tissue forming the major part of a tooth.

Diadochokinesia (DIE-ah-DOE-koh-ki-nee-see-ah). The function of arresting one motor impulse and substituting another diametrically opposite.

Diaphragm (DYE-uh-fram). The muscular and tendonous partition separating the abdominal and thoracic cavities.

Diarthrosis (die-ARTH-throw-sis). A joint surrounded by a cavity thus enabling it to have diverse movement; a freely moving joint such as the elbow or wrist.

Digastric Muscle (die-GAS-tric) Refer to index.

Distoclusion (DIS-toe-clue-shun). Malocclusion in which the lower jaw is displaced backward in relation to the upper teeth.

Dorsum. The upper and posterior portion of a surface; especially of the tongue.

Dura Mater (DUE-rah may-ter). Encloses brain and spinal cord; two layers separated by a venous sinus; at foramen magnum the outer layer continues as the periosteum on the outer surface of skull and the inner layer passes down spinal cord.

Efferent. Conveying away from the center.

Electromyogram (i-leck-tro-MIGH-o-gram). Tracings showing electrical response in a contracting muscle.

Eleidin (el-E-i-din). The semifluid, acidophil material in the stratum lucidum of the epidermis, resulting in transparency of lips.

Endocrine (EN-do-kren). Secreting internally.

Endolymph (EN-doh-limf). Fluid in inner ear (scala media).

Enzyme (EN-zeyem). A complex organic compound secreted by living cells; capable of causing or accelerating some change in its substrate, for which it is often specific.

Epiglottis (ep-i-GLOT-tis). A lid-like cartilage, shaped like a bicycle seat, covering the entrance to the laryngeal cavity.

Epinephrine (EP-eh-NEF-rin). Active principle of the medullary portion of the adrenal glands; adrenalin.

Epithelium (epeh-THEE-lee-um). The cellular outer surface of skin and mucous membrane which is without blood supply.

Epiphyses (ee-PIFF-i-seez). Piece of bone separated from a long bone in early life by cartilage, but later becomes part of the larger bone.

Epithelial Tissue (eph-uh-THEEL-ee-al). Cells joined by small amounts of cementing substance; lines cavities and covers outer surface of body.

Eustachian Tube (you-STAY-kee-un). The tube leading from the middle ear to the nasopharynx; named in honor of Eustachius, a sixteenth century Italian anatomist.

Extrinsic (ex-TRIN-sic). Originating outside of a part.

Falx Cerebri (falks SIR-eh-bree). A fold of the inner layer of dura mater separating the two cerebral hemispheres as far down as the corpus callosum.

Fasciculus (fas-IK-you-lus). A small bundle of nerve fibers gathering to make up whole nerves.

Fauces (FAW-seez). Passage between the mouth and pharynx.

Flaccid (FLAK-sid). Soft; applied to muscles which have lost their tonus.

Foramen (for-A-men). A perforation or opening.

Frenulum (FREE-new-lum). Small fold of integument or mucous membrane checking or limiting the movement of an organ or part.

Frequency. The number of cycles or times per second an object vibrates.

Fricative. Refers to a speech sound produced by forcing an air stream through a narrow opening.

Funiculus (fun-IK-you-lus). A bundle of fibers; less specific functionally than a fasciculus.

Ganglion (GANG-lee-on). A concentration of nerve-cell bodies serving as nervous centers.

Genioglossus Muscle (je-ni-o-GLAH-sus). Refer to index.

Geniohyoid Muscle (je-ni-o-HIGH-oid). Refer to index.

Glossal (GLAHS-al). Pertaining to the tongue.

Glossopalatinus Muscle (glos-so-pal-uh-TEE-nus). Refer to index.

Glottis (GLAH-tis). The area between the open vocal folds.

Grey Matter Masses. Composed of nerve cells (as opposed to white matter, composed of nerve fibers); largest and most important of the masses within cerebral hemisphere are: caudate nucleus, lenticular nucleus, thalamus.

Helicotrema (HEL-eh-ko-TREE-mah). Passage connecting scala tympani and scala vestibuli at the apex of the cochlea.

Hormone. A chemical secretion of the ductless glands carried in the blood stream and acting to stimulate the activity of organs.

Hyaline (HIGH-ah-lin). A flexible, slightly elastic and semi transparent type of cartilage.

Hyoepiglottic Ligament (high-o-ep-i-GLAH-tic). Connects the hyoid bone to the epiglottis.

Hyoglossus Muscle (high-o-GLAH-sus). Refer to index.

Hyoid (HIGH-oid). The U shaped bone located below the tongue.

Hypothalamus (high-poe-THAL-a-mus). A small but important area of grey matter in the floor of the third ventricle. Closely connected functionally and structurally with the pituitary gland; it affects the activities of the cerebrum, thalamus, subcortical motor nuclei and the ANS; among its more detailed functions are (a) control of water balance, (b) regulates appetite to link intake of food with demands of body, (c) regulates body temperature (d) concerned with production and control of emotional reactions.

Iliocostalis Muscle (i-lee-o-cos-TAL-iss). A division of the sacrospinalis muscle.

Ilium (ILL-ee-um). Hip bone.

Inertia (in-NER-shah). That property of matter by which matter at rest tends to remain at rest, or matter in motion tends to remain in motion unless acted upon by an external force.

Infrahyoid (in-frah-HIGH-oid). Situated below the hyoid bone.

Insula (IN-su-la). "The island of Reil." A lobe infolded between the frontal and temporal lobes, not showing on surface of hemisphere; one of the five lobes of the cerebrum; lies deep in lateral sulcus.

Integument (in-TEG-you-ment). A covering; of the body: the skin.

Intrinsic (in-TRIN-sic). Anything wholly contained within another structure; usually applies to muscles exclusively attached to one organ or structure, as intrinsic muscles of the tongue.

Isthmus (ISS-mus). Narrow strip of tissue or narrow passage containing two larger parts.

Lamina (LAM-i-nah). A thin flat plate or layer.

Larynx (LAH-rinks). The cartilaginous and muscular structure at the top of the trachea and below the tongue roots and hyoid bone containing the vocal folds.

Laryngopharynx (la-ring-go-FA-rinks). The lower portion of the pharynx lying between the hyoid and cricoid cartilage.

Latissimus Dorsi Muscle (la-TIS-si-mus DOR-see). The widest muscle of the back. Refer to index.

Lenticular (lentiform) **Nucleus** (len-TIC-u-lar). A roughly lens-shaped mass of grey matter in forebrain divided by thin sheets of white matter (fibers) into the putamen, the outer layer, and the globus pallidus, the inner part; together with caudate nucleus referred to as corpus striatum or basal ganglia.

Levator Ani Muscle (le-VA-tor AN-i). The chief muscle of the pelvic diaphragm. Refer to index.

Levatores Costraum Muscles (LEV-ah-TOR-es kahs-TAR-um). Refer to index.

Levator Scapulae Muscle (le-VA-tor SCAP-u-lie). Refer to index.

Levator Veli Palatini Muscle (LE-va-tor VE-li PAL-uh-TEE-ne). Refer to index.

Ligament (LIG-a-ment). Tough, fibrous connective bands supporting bones and viscera.

Linea Alba (LIN-e-a AL-ba). A tendinous raphe extending in the median line of the abdomen from the pubes to the xiphoid process; it is formed by the blending of the aponeuroses of the oblique and transverse muscles.

Lingual (LIN-gual). Pertaining to the tongue.

Longissimus Dorsi Muscle (long-GIS-see-muss DOR-see). The longest of the three divisions of the sacrospinalis muscle. Refer to index.

Longitudinalis Inferior Muscle (lon-gi-tu-di-NAL-is). Refer to index.

Longitudinalis Superior Muscle. Refer to index.

Lumbar Puncture. To obtain specimens of cerebrospinal fluid; a needle is inserted into back between the spinous processes of either the 3rd and 4th or 4th and 5th lumbar vertebrae and through the dura mater into the subarachnoid space; the fluid pressure is measured by a monometer attached to needle; pressures over 200 mm are regarded as abnormal.

Lumen (LU-men). Cavity or channel within a tube or tubular organ.

Malleus (MAY-lee-us). Tiny bone in middle ear.

Mandible (MAN-di-ble). Horseshoe shaped bone forming the jaw.

Mandibular Symphasis (man-DI-bu-lar SYM-fah-sis). The midpoint of the chin marking the junction between the two halves of the mandible.

Manubrium (mah-NEW-bree-um). Handle shaped structure usually related to uppermost portion of the sternum and the inferior portion of the malleus.

Masseter Muscle (mas-SEE-ter). Refer to index.

Meatus (me-A-tus). A passageway.

Mediastinum (mee-di-ah-STEYE-num). A median partition; usually applied to the median septum dividing the thorax into two lateral cavities.

Medulla Oblongata (meh-DUL-ah ab-long-GAH-tah). The most inferior portion of the brain stem; where it connects with the spinal cord.

Membrane (MEM-brane). A thin layer of tissue covering or dividing organs and surfaces.

Meniere's Disease (men-a-AIRZ). Hearing loss, tinnitus, and dizziness occurring in assocation with nonsuppurative disease of the labyrinth.

Mentalis Muscle (men-TAL-is). A muscle related to movement of the lower lip. Refer to index.

Mental Protuberance (pro-TU-ber-ance). The medial elevation on the body of the mandible.

Mesenteric (mes-in-TER-ik). Pertaining to the peritoneal fold attaching to the intestine to the posterior abdominal wall.

Mesiocclusion (me-si-o-CLUE-shun). Malocclusion of the teeth in which the mandibular teeth are in an anterior relationship to the maxillary teeth.

Midbrain. A very much smaller area of brain than the cerebrum; about 2 cm long; sandwiched between the forebrain (which has overgrown it) and the hindbrain.

Modiolus (mo-DIE-o-lus). Center pillar of the cochlea.

Myelinated (medullated). **Nerve Fibers** (MY-lehn-ate-ted). Consist of an axon surrounded by a myelinated sheath enclosing the axon very much as an electric wire is enclosed in a plastic covering; white fibers.

Myelination (medullation) **of Nerve Fibers.** Begins at 6th month of intrauterine life in spinal cord; sensory fibers are myelinated before motor fibers; in the "association area" of brain myelination continues to take place up to about 18 years.

Mylohyoid Muscle (my-lo-HIGH-oid). Refer to index.

Myxedema (mik-seh-DEE-mah). Swelling of face and hands as result of deficient functioning of thyroid gland.

Nasopharynx (na-zo-FA-rinks). The portion of the pharynx above the soft palate.

Natural or Free Period. The frequency at which a vibrating body vibrates at greatest ease.

Nerve Tracts. Bundles of fibers performing a common function, starting from one place in nervous system and going to another; they are stationary and when one says nerve tracts go here or there, one is describing the course taken by the nervous impulse in them; names of the tracts often describe their beginning-end (corticothalamic fibers run from cortex to thalamus).

Neurofibrils. Fine fibers through which nervous impulses are belived to pass as they go through the neuron (cell).

Neuroglia (nyour-OG-li-ah). Nonnervous cells which form the "packing" or support for nerve cells.

Neurolemma (nu-ro-LEM-ah). A thin, membraneous covering enclosing each peripheral fiber and its medullary sheath.

Neuron (NU-run). Nerve cell with its processes.

Node of Ranvier (RAN-vee-air). That point where the myelinated sheath and axon are compressed circularly; happens about every millimeter both in central and peripheral system.

Noise. A complex sound having many frequencies not in mutual harmonious relation.

Nucleus (NEW-klee-us). Small, round body within each cell acting as the functional control center; also masses of cell bodies in brain or spinal cord.

Oblique Arytenoid Muscle (o-BLEEK- air e-TEE-noid). Refer to index.

Occipital Lobe (ahk-SIP-eh-tal). Forms the posterior end of the cerebral hemisphere and lies above the cerebellum from which it is separated by a shelf of dura mater; it contains the visual area of cortex.

Occlusion (o-CLUE-zhun). A closing or shutting up; the state of being closed or shut.

Omohyoid Muscle (o-mo-HIGH-oid). Refer to index.

Optic Chiasma (keye-AS-mah). The converging of the fibers of the optic nerves.

Orbicularis Oris Muscle (or-bik-u-LAH-ris OR-is). Refer to index.

Oropharynx (o-ro-FA-rinks). That portion of the pharynx extending from the level of the hyoid bone to the soft palate.

Ossicle (AHS-i-kull). A small bone; usually applied to the bones of the ear.

Overtones. Any partial in a complex tone.

Pectoralis Major Muscle (pek-toe-RA-lis). Refer to index.

Pectoralis Minor Muscle. Refer to index.

Peduncle (ped-DUNG-kul). A supporting part of another structure; usually applied to the bands running between sections of brain.

Perilymph (PER-e-limf). Fluid contained in space between osseous and membranous labyrinth of the inner ear.

Periosteum (per-i-AHS-te-um). The fibrous membrane surrounding the surfaces of bones, except at the points of tendinous and ligamentous attachment and on the articular surfaces, where cartilage is substituted.

Pharyngeal (fah-RIN-gee-ull). Pertaining to the pharynx or throat.

Pharynx (FA-rinks). A musculomembranous, pouch-like structure extending from base of skull to the level of the sixth cervical vertebrae; it opens into the mouth, posterior nares, eustachian tubes, esophagus, and trachea. It consists of three main divisions: laryngopharynx, oropharynx, and the nasopharynx.

Pharyngopalatinus Muscle (fah-ring-go-PAL-uh-TEE-nus). Refer to index.

Phonation (foe-NA-shun). The production of voiced sounds resulting from vocal fold vibrations.

Phoneme (FOE-neem). A group or family of closely related speech sounds all of which have the same distinctive acoustic characteristics.

Phones. Individual speech sounds.

Phrenic (FREN-ik). Pertaining to the mind or diaphragm; usually applied to the special spinal nerve supplying the diaphragm.

Phrenic Nerve. A nerve emerging from the cervical plexus from fibers C3, 4 and 5; runs down neck into thorax, passes in front of the root of the lung and supplies diaphragm.

Pitch. The psychological perception of the frequency of vibrating matter.

Platsyma Muscle (plah-TIZ-muh). Refer to index.

Pleura (PLOOR-ah). Serous membrane covering the lungs and lining the thoracic cavity.

Plexuses (PLEX-sus). A complicated gathering station; the anterior branches of the cervical, lumbar and sacral nerves combine to form complicated plexuses from which individual nerves, of mixed (sensory and motor) composition, emerge and travel to the parts they supply.

Posterior Cricoarytenoid Ligament (Cry-ko-air-e-Tee-noid). Refer to index.

Proprioceptive (pro-pree-o-SEP-tive). Refers to receiving stimulations within the tissues of the body; in muscles and tendons.

Pterygoid (TER-i-goyd). Shaped like a wing.

Quadratus Labii Inferioris Muscle (quad-RAH-tus LAY-bee). Refer to index.

Quadratus Labii Superioris Muscle. Refer to index.

Quadratus Lumborum Muscle (quad-RA-tus- lum-BORE-um). Refer to index.

Raphe (RAY-fee). A ridge marking the union between halves of symmetrical parts.

Rectus Abdominus Muscle (REK-tus ab-DAH-meh-nus). Refer to index.

Reticular (reh-TIK-u-lar). Like a network; usually applied to the network of fibers passing between the pons and the medulla.

Rhomboideus Major Muscle (rhom-BOY-de-us). Refer to index.

Rhomboideus Minor Muscle. Refer to index.

Sacrospinalis Muscle (SA-krow-spy-NA-lis). Refer to index.

Sagittal (SAD-gi-tal). One of the planes into which the body is divided; straight—usually applied to the plane dividing body into right and left portions.

Salpingopharyngeus Muscle (sal-ping-go-fa-RIN-jee-us). Refer to index.

Scalenus Muscle (skay-LEE-nus). Refer to index.

Septum (SEP-tum). A partition or dividing wall—the nasal septum.

Serratus (ser-RAH-tus). Serrated; formed with teeth like a saw; name given various muscles.

Sinus (SIGN-us). A hollow or cavity; a recess or pocket. A cavity within a bone.

Sonant. A voiced speech sound.

Sphenoid (SFEE-noid). Wedge-shaped; applied to complex bone of interior skull.

Sphincter (SFINGK-ter). A ring-like muscle (s) closing a natural opening.

Splanchnic (SPLANK-nik). Pertaining to the viscera.

Sternocleidomastoideus Muscle (ster-no-kli-do-mas-TOID-de-us). Refer to index.

Stretch Reflex. The contraction of a muscle in response to sudden stretching; if a muscle is stretched, it responds reflexively by contracting; as a result of stretch reflexes, the body is maintained in an upright position by varying degrees of tone in different muscles.

Stylopharyngeus Muscle (sty-lo-fa-RIN-jee-us). Refer to index.

Subarachnoid Space (sub-ah-RACK-noid). Between the arachnoid mater and pia mater; filled with cerebrospinal fluid; due to the arachnoid membrane passing on top of the gyri and the pia mater dipping down into the folds of every sulcus thus creating a space between.

Subclavius Muscle (sub-CLA-vi-us). Refer to index.

Subcostal Muscles (sub-KAHS-tal). Refer to index.

Substantia Ossea (sub-STAN-she-ah AH-see-uh). Cementum of the teeth.

Surd. A voiceless speech sound.

Symphyses (SIM-fi-sis). Usually applied to a line formed by the union of two bones; more definite than a suture.

Synapse (SIN-apse). A functional connection between two neurons so that impulses may pass from one to the other.

Synarthrosis (sin-ARTH-throw-sis). An immovable or slightly movable joint lacking a cavity at the joint.

Synovial Fluid (sin-NOV-vee-al). A lubricant for joints secreted by the internal layer of the articular capsule surrounding the joint cavity.

Tensor Veli Palatini Muscle (TEN-sor ve-li pal-uh-TEE-nee). Refer to index.

Thalamus (THAL-a-mus). A large egg-shaped mass of grey matter in the diencephalon; a relay station on the sensory line to the cortex.

Thoracic Cavity (tho-RAS-ik). The chest; the portion of the body between the clavicle superiorly and the diaphragm inferiorly; sometimes referred to as the thoracic cage.

Thyroarytenoid Muscle (thy-ro-air-e-TEE-noid). Refer to index.

Thyroepiglottic Muscle (thy-ro-ep-i-GLAH-tic). Refer to index.

Thyroid (THY-roid). The shield-shaped cartilage of the larynx; also a gland.

Tonus (TONE-us). Muscle tone (balance) resulting from stimulation of muscles in varying degrees; that degree of tension each muscle exhibits and by means of which posture is maintained.

Trachea (TRAY-kee-ah). The windpipe; a cartilaginous and membranous tube connecting the larynx and bronchi.

Transversus Linguae Muscle (LING-gwigh). Refer to index.

Trapezius Muscle (trah-PEE-zi-us). Refer to index.

Triangularis Muscle tri-an-gu-LA-ris). Refer to index.

Turbinated (TER-bin-a-ted). Top-shaped bone, filled with hollows and pits.

Tympanic Membrane (tim-PAN-ick). The ear drum or membrane separating the external ear from the middle ear.

Upper Motor Neuron. A motor fiber with the CNS.

Uvulae Muscle (UV-u-lie). An unpaired muscle forming the greater part of the uvula. Refer to index.

Uvula (YOUV-you-lah). Pendent, fleshy mass; uvula palatina.

Vagus Nerve (VA-gus). The 10th cranial nerve; supplies pharynx, larynx, esophagus, heart, bronchi, lungs, among others; the only cranial nerve supplying areas other than head and neck.

Velum (VEE-lum). Considered synonymous with the soft palate: also considered as the most posterior portion of the soft palate.

Ventricle (VEN-tree-kol). A small cavity.

Ventricular Folds (ven-TRIK-you-lar). Another name for the false vocal folds forming the medial margins of the quadrangular membrane.

Viscera (VIS-er-ah). Large interior organs in any of the three large body cavities; especially in the abdomen.

Vital Capacity. The maximum volume of air which may be expired following a maximal inspiration.

Vocalis Muscle (vo-KA-lis). Refer to index.

Xiphoid Process (ZIGH-foid). Most inferior portion of the sternum or breastbone.

Zygomaticus Muscle (zigh-go-MA-ti-kus). Refer to index.

INDEX

N

O

P

Q

R

S

T